Add.

THE BUSINESS OF FARMING

THE BUSINESS
OF FARMING

BY HERRELL DEGRAFF
AND LADD HAYSTEAD

NORMAN : UNIVERSITY OF OKLAHOMA PRESS : 1948

Foreword

I LIKE this book. The authors say it is not "delightful." They assume it will not interest readers who like to bask in the romance of country life without regard to costs. Those of us with a bit of Scotch blood find that profits in farming add to the romance of farm ownership and operation. Hence, *The Business of Farming* is a delightful book. Making money adds to the fascination of farming.

It is refreshing to read farm management so easily and find complicated principles discussed with such clarity. For example, soils are basic. More than any other factor, they "Will Make—Or Break—You." Labor is the highest cost item on farms—even though it is that of the operator or his family. "Your labor is worth what it produces"—a fact too little appreciated by farmers. The many factors that control farm profits are indeed "crazy-quilt pieces," until brought into a definite farm-operating plan.

This book is filled with reality. There is constant suggestion that problems be faced squarely. If necessary, change the type of farming; if soils or size seriously limit the chance to "make a decent living," get part-time work off the farm or sell the farm and buy another.

The size of a farm is more appropriately measured in terms of the volume of business rather than the number of acres. Many persons may be startled to realize that "too small farms" make up almost three-fourths of the total. They do not adequately support a family. Among these are "rural slums" as pitiful as those which exist in the cities.

Every person who expects to enter farming with less than $10,000 capital should study Chapter 23. Entirely too many people fall victims to small-acreage or cheap-land propaganda. "How Big A Job Can A Small Farm Offer?" The answer, in most cases, as the authors show, is "not big enough." It applies now to thousands of industrial workers and G. I.'s who have already spent their savings for a "cheap" farm. It will apply to thousands of others when industry disgorges during the next depression.

v

". . . only about a third of all farm operators make as much for their own labor and management as the going rate of hired hands' wages."

Management certainly begins with the selection of the farm.

The authors could have been more specific in many instances. Soil ratings are referred to, but the national and state systems that can be so helpful to laymen, as well as to farmers, have not been explained. The chapter on tillage implements leaves one with a feeling that more questions have been raised than answers offered. Many guideposts are included, but many which professional farm managers and farm operators use almost daily are absent.

You, too, will like this book if you are a friend of the land and a realist about farming. Agriculture is the balance wheel of the nation. Intelligent farm management, more than any other factor, will maintain the productivity of the land and keep farmers from peasantry. Their economic well-being will insure their continued sound social attitude which, in turn, will help maintain national stability.

TRUE D. MORSE
President, Doane Agricultural Service, Inc.
Editor, "Doane Agricultural Digest"
St. Louis, Missouri

The Authors Criticize the Authors

THIS is not a delightful book.

If you would thoughtfully and pleasantly savor the poetry of the fields, read no further. If you want your farming to be a maximum of katydids, of lazy hours under a vine-shaded porch, of rich rewards in country smells, country tastes, and country feelings, these pages will be of little help.

Whatever the authors may think or feel about farming as an emotional experience, they rigorously have left the reader out of their confidence. They do not suggest that farming is the best of all living, nor that just anybody can succeed at it even though he may follow with slavish intensity the ground rules and hints as set down here.

The farming the writers are talking about is a serious, possibly even a cold, business proposition entered into with the primary intention of making a profit. True, a reader may want to farm because he thinks it is the best way to rear children, or because he believes farming is a healthful pursuit, or just because he does not like cities. Usually, after he has satisfied such an urge, he then wants to make a profit if possible. In that case, we can offer him some help—but only on the business side.

We have no quarrel with anybody who wants to take his farming as a spiritual assuagement. We read and enjoy the many books whose titles suggest farming as a way of life for almost every reason in the world except material gain. And there is little doubt that the lives of many have been enriched in finding a farm a refuge from commercialism and the mighty American urge to turn everything into a dollar. Surely, it is a happy thing for the country that we have so many acres we can well afford to dedicate some part of our lands to recreation, to spiritual welfare, and to rural shrines of peace. And it is well for the human race that from Cato, Columella, and Varro down to Louis Bromfield there have been gifted writers to extol the virtues of the land as the fountainhead of poesy, song, and rustic simplicity in living.

Yet, as young farming America goes through the painful

process of choosing a vocation, as ever increasing numbers of city men turn to the farm as an investment, a business different from their usual pursuits, both groups are confronted with the hard fact that neither creditors nor tax collectors will accept an ode or epode as full satisfaction of accounts. Some place along the line the oldest honored profession must show a profit in a material sense if the aesthetic values are to be of a permanent or recurring nature.

That is the job, narrow though it be in a literary sense, that we have set our hands to. Unlike the goodly company of very competent writers who have sought to explore the far bounds of this field, we have tried to stick to the bare fundamentals, simplifying the ever growing complexities of the topic. Our goal has been not to study and expound the intricacies of the many new developments in management that fill each month's issues of the farm press. Rather, we have tried to take the new, break it down, dissect it, and then fit it into the confines of the basic pattern.

There are many subjects we do not treat that seem to be "musts" in other works. Such willful omission is not a cavalier dismissal of the matters as worthless. On the contrary, we heartily recommend in many footnotes and suggestions in the main copy that these topics be pursued elsewhere. But here we have tried to stick to the three underlying factors without which, as we see it, all other items become leaves unattached to a parent tree.

This stubborn insistence in relating the myriad facets of one of the most complex businesses in the world to three simple factors is no academic primering. It stems directly from actual experiences on many farms in many states with many farmers, particularly those who are either young or newly come to the business.

As so many new gadgets, processes, and theories come along in what seems to be a swelling flood, those of limited experience tend to look for the easy way to solve all problems. That is, rather than go to the onerous business of analysis, digging for first causes, modifying influences, and probable effects, the modern way is to telephone to town for quick delivery of a machine, a chemical, or a political unguent. Perhaps the "new way" will cure a symptom or so, maybe it will even get at the cause, but the farmer who does not understand his basic needs will lose many dollars in what may turn out to be rather futile research on a one-man scale.

A case in point is the "vo-ag" student on his first venture who thinks DDT will protect his orchard from almost all pests and never mind such a dull grind as studying life cycles and habits of the bugs. Perhaps DDT will keep him a jump or so ahead of his enemies, but destroying host trees and bushes in the fence rows might well be the more profitable act. And there is that man from the city who believes that all farmers are fifty years behind the times and need "a business man's approach" if they are to survive. He puts his faith in pedigrees, fine structures, an "enlightened" labor policy, and does not know as Cato did that success lies in the master's eye (providing the master has trained his eye to see).

Technological advances are changing farming at a rate never seen before in all history. New machines, strains, and techniques are very truly limiting—but not eliminating—the gamble in agriculture. Moreover, we know now that the hard way is not necessarily the right way, as we also know that all of the new things put together have not made farming the easiest way of life. But fundamentals are not changing. We are merely learning more about them, why they are and what we can do to get into consonance with them. When you strip the verbiage from tomorrow's newest "revolutionary theory," more than likely you will find something that may add to your understanding, give a salutary fillip to your thinking, but probably will not greatly shake your faith in the three fundamentals of soils, plants, and animals, and the person who does the job. Though the new be fascinating, it can be of greatest help if we remember Santayana's observation that the man who ignores history is fated to repeat it.

The Authors Thank

Among the many debts we owe, probably our first bow should go to ancient Cato. Maybe Jethro Tull should come next and Justus von Liebig not far behind. Certainly all of us modern Americans should remember that Washington and Jefferson made contributions to our farm management, if not as important as their political gifts, still of great worth.

Of course, it is our contemporaries who have us under greatest obligation. Particularly are we indebted to Professors Ivan R. Bierly and S. W. Warren of Cornell University for many hours of discussion on farm-management problems both large and small, and for constructive criticism throughout the preparation of the manuscript.

Thanks are due to Professors Richard Bradfield and Marlin G. Cline of Cornell and Professor J. A. Slipher of Ohio State University for valuable aid and suggestions on soil management. Professor Firman Bear of Rutgers University and his publishers, John Wiley and Son, graciously gave permission to quote from any of Dr. Bear's authoritative works on soil chemistry. Professor William Albrecht of the University of Missouri kindly read and checked the manuscript.

Our deep appreciation goes to George Krieger, ASAE, of Ethyl Corporation, and Frank Zink, ASAE, of Frank Zink Associates, Consulting Agricultural Engineers, for their help, suggestions, and criticisms on the equipment section. D. A. Milligan of Harry Ferguson, Inc., and Archie Stone, author of several works on farm machinery, now with the Chinese government as expert on modern equipment, also furnished greatly appreciated data and advice.

Professors T. N. Hurd of Cornell, L. S. Hardin of Purdue, R. E. L. Greene of North Carolina State, Max Brunk of the University of Florida, and George T. Blanch of Utah State gave unstintingly of their energies to supply facts and critical help on labor management.

To Professors R. M. Carter of the University of Vermont, K. T. Wright of Michigan State, E. H. Matzen of the University of Missouri, M. T. Buchanan and A. W. Peterson of Washington State, Arthur Bratton of Cornell, and Dr. D. B. Ferguson of Swift and Company, our thanks for carrying on long, thoughtful, and exceptionally helpful correspondence and discussion.

So many others have contributed supporting data, case histories, and wise counsel that it is impossible to name them all. But we are especially indebted to D. Howard Doane of the Doane Agricultural Service, to Bruce Russell of the Farmers National (management service), to Patricia Damp for digging source material and checking data, and to Margaret McConnell for copyreading and managing the manuscript.

To each of the publishers and authors who have so graciously permitted us to quote from them, our thanks.

In particular, we appreciate the use of material from the following volumes: *Theory and Practice in the Use of Fertilizers,* by

Firman E. Bear, published by John Wiley & Sons., Inc.; Wilson
Gee, *The Social Economics of Agriculture,* copyright 1932 and
1942 by The Macmillan Company; H. C. Taylor, *Outlines of
Agricultural Economics,* copyright 1919, 1925, and 1931 by The
Macmillan Company; Charles E. Kellogg, *The Soils That Support
Us,* copyright 1941 by The Macmillan Company; and Robert R.
Hudelson, *Farm Management,* copyright 1939 by The Macmillan
Company, and used with their permission. We are also grateful to
Mr. William D. Geer, publisher of *Fortune,* who gave permission
for the reprinting of several quotations from The Farm Column.

We feel especially honored and are accordingly most appreci-
ative that True D. Morse, president of Doane Agricultural Service
and one of the nation's outstanding professional farm managers,
consented to provide the trenchant foreword which so well sets
the stage for what follows.

October, 1947   Herrell DeGraff
                                                        Ithaca, New York

                                                        Ladd Haystead
                                                        Wallkill, New York

Contents

Illustrations

Charts, Graphs, and Tables

THE BUSINESS OF FARMING

PART I: Soil Management

*"Success or failure in farming
starts with the soil."*

1. The Soil Will Make—or Break—You!

YOU can have good soil and poor soil management, and you may fail. You can have poor soil and poor management, and you will fail certainly. But though your soil may not be the best, with good management your chances of success can be better than a mere gamble.

Because there is a great deal more poor soil than good soil in these United States, this section deals with what a good manager can do to enhance his profits by proper soil management. Even a poor soil does not of itself mean failure. It does mean that one has to work harder, plan more wisely, and execute more smartly than his neighbor on good soil. Rule-of-thumb methods or superstitions, however venerable, are not substitutes for adequate practices of soil improvement.

It is rare to find two farms that are alike; even rarer to find two farmers alike. Soil types are numbered in the thousands; and farmers' ways of handling the soil are almost as numerous as farmers themselves. In many sections of the country it is impossible to find two fields with the same soil type; it is even common to find several soil types in one field. What to do about such soil differences not only is the basis of good management, it may also be the inexorable director of what kind of farming operation one chooses.

Many an American farmer has been sold out by the sheriff because he tried to carry on a type of farming for which his soil was not suited. He has said, "I'm a truck farmer," and has gone to truck farming on lands suited only for extensive livestock raising. Or he has tried to grow orchards on lands that would support only trees for timber. Or, perhaps the greatest of all examples of wrong soil usages, he plowed up plains that nature meant only for graz-

3

ing lands. He turned those acres to small grains and corn, and went bankrupt in the drought years that followed the breaking of the lands.

Success or failure in farming starts with the soil. Thus, good farm management must start with consideration of the soils.

The husbandry of soil is the very essence of agriculture. Farming in all its variations centers around the production of plants. Even the stockman whose main interest is his animals—he, too, has built his business upon the soil. His livestock are merely the means by which he markets the plant growth his soil produces.

Soil is much more than just dirt. It is far more than the mere decomposition product of the rocks of the earth. It is a complex body of material having definite though variable form and character. It provides an anchorage for plant roots that enable the plants not only to grow upright but to grow at all. It furnishes them with the essential moisture for their life processes and with the vital mineral elements for their growth.

Soils did not occur originally as we find them now. They have a history of development, ages long, from a simple beginning to a complex maturity. They have been conditioned by the rocks from which they develop and, even more, by environment. In America, all but the very end of that history was under an environment of nature. Natural processes, undisturbed by man, were the influences of development. Man has modified the work of nature, and all too often his modification has been destructive.

This fact has only recently received wide recognition, but it is now deplored by those thoughtful few who look analytically at tomorrow's America. Only in the last decade has the American public developed any degree of general soil consciousness. That it is now developing, as many soil scientists believe, is a significant fact in our national life. An expanding pioneer economy and a consciousness of resource conservation are social phenomena that do not go together. In recent years we have been passing from one to the other, and the consciousness of this fact is the most potent of all signs of a national coming-of-age. It is a milestone announcing our approach to an economic optimum of population, to which we have never before given thought. This comment does not mean that the writers join the mourners over the closing of America's

4

physical frontier. The frontier has merely moved from the open spaces to the laboratory, where the opportunities on which America must progress will be born and nurtured.

But at least one of our frontiers cannot move indoors, cannot be supplanted by a laboratory product. That is the soil. Hydroponics, the nutrient-culture method of plant production that might refute this statement, must for the immediate future remain more a laboratory curiosity than a commercial alternative to traditional farming.[1]

No longer can we move on west to take up new lands to replace the soils ruined by unwise farming. Nor does any considerable acreage capable of development exist that was passed over on the westward trek. On into the indefinite future we must farm substantially on the soils now under cultivation.

Our acreage has changed very little in the last few decades. In 1930 we had 6,288,648 farms with a total of 986,771,000 acres. In 1940 we had 6,096,799 farms with an acreage of 1,060,852,000. But, significantly, cropland harvested in 1929 was 359,000,000 acres, while that in 1939 was 321,000,000. In other words, farms are growing fewer in number and larger in total acreage, but cultivated lands show some decrease. This reflects the land taken out of production which has been eroded, abandoned, or never should have been tilled in the first place.

All citizens, not just farmers alone, have a stake in the proper maintenance and use of our soils. They are as much the source of life in industrial America as they were in colonial America. Not only the traditional food and fiber but other raw materials of industry in increasing variety and quantity must come from them.

Certainly the present generation more than any other has a big stake in soil maintenance for its own future well-being. And

[1] Readers of the farm press may question this statement because of the publicity given to the army's big hydroponics plant on Ascension Island. True, that experiment was highly successful in producing food where no orthodox agriculture is possible. However, costs of production were not the army's worry, particularly when transportation costs were even higher. Commercially, the hydroponics farms in California and Maryland have yet to prove themselves. Unless land prices were to go beyond any cost conceivable, the steady lowering of unit costs of production which has taken place in recent years suggests that advocates of the hydroponic process must travel a rocky road to get into successful competition with traditional production methods.

5

the generations to follow will inherit only what we pass on. Our objective should be to so use our soils that our descendants may say we considered wisely and acted well.

We speak quite unthinkingly of "old soils" and "virgin soils." We refer, of course, to the length of time the land has been farmed. Actually the virgin soil is as old, geologically, as soils that have been under tillage for many generations. We once watched the breaking of a piece of land that never before had known the plow. The owner told us that he was looking forward to much higher yields from that field than he was obtaining from other parts of his farm. "I've heard my grandfather tell," he said, "of enormous yields of corn on fields newly cleared from the woods." The woods had been removed years before from the field he was plowing and it had since been used for pasture. "We will be harvesting virgin fertility," he said.

Yet the only difference between that field and his other land was cultivation for less than one hundred years. The processes of nature had been at work for thousands of years to develop that soil as the pioneering farmer found it, but in a minute fraction of that time (under "mining" processes) it had declined in productivity. Must it be that all soils should rapidly deteriorate under tillage? If so, then what we have called farming has, in truth, been mining. And mining is essentially a process of taking all and giving back nothing.

A study in Ohio points this up most forcefully. State-wide yield figures for corn, oats, wheat, and hay were charted by ten-year periods from the eighteen seventies through the nineteen twenties. Over that period of sixty years, corn yields remained practically unchanged, and oat, wheat, and hay yields increased moderately. Studied superficially, the figures show no cause for concern about the maintenance of soil productivity. However, on closer examination it is apparent that many improvements in farm practice since 1870 should have increased average yields materially. Improved and higher-yielding varieties of crops, greater use of lime and fertilizers, an increased use of legumes in rotation, new power machines that do a better job of seedbed preparation, cultivation, and harvesting than was done by the displaced animal-powered machines, better control of pests and diseases, and the retirement from agriculture of many unproductive acres—these are among

6

the contributions to a better agriculture that should have boosted average yields.

The authors of this study say:

"Certainly, taken together, all of these changes and improvements should have raised acre yields considerably—how much it is difficult to say exactly, but we believe an increase of 40 to 60 per cent would have been conservative.

"For example, wheat yields were only 3.2 bushels more during the decade of 1920–29 than in the seventies. Four-fifths of Ohio's wheat acreage is now planted to improved varieties which yield, according to hundreds of field tests and thousands of threshermen's records, 3 or 4 bushels more per acre than the varieties they displaced. From 1920 to 1929, the average acre of wheat in Ohio annually received about 180 pounds of fertilizer, and we know from hundreds of field tests that this alone should have increased the yield at least 7 bushels. Taken together, fertilizers and better varieties should have increased the yield 10 bushels, as against an actual increase of only 3 bushels.

"There can be but one explanation for the stubbornness with which acre yields have resisted the farmers' efforts to improve them. The natural productive capacity of the land has been deteriorating at a rate almost fast enough to offset all of these improvements in soil and crop management. With every step ahead we have slipped back almost if not quite as far."[2] (See chart on page 33.)

Of the bountiful and varied resources with which our country has been blessed, only the soil produces a continuing yield, an annually recurring harvest. Other major resources (the minerals and mineral fuels), once used, are possessions we had and enjoyed but cannot use again. From agriculture we can literally eat our cake and have it, too. Thus our soil becomes the more precious as our insatiable industrial machine eats more heavily into our non-agricultural resources. But an "if" remains to be considered—an "if" of major proportions. The soil can continue its output without dimunition only *if* its fertility is maintained.

Continuous change characterizes the natural history of a soil. Under the forces of nature the changes take place slowly, being

[2] R. M. Salter, R. D. Lewis, and J. A. Slipher, *Our Heritage—the Soil* (Ohio State University Agricultural Extension Bulletin 175, April, 1936), 5.

7

measured by geological rather than by calendar time. Essentially, because soils have a history of change, they obviously have a future that will be characterized by further change. Under cultivation they change more rapidly than in an undisturbed natural environment. The farmer makes them more productive or less productive; the degree of improvement or depletion is determined by his management. One of the four requirements of a good farmer set forth by Liberty Hyde Bailey is that he shall leave his farm "more productive than it was when he took it." Primarily that means his soils must be more productive. No greater goal could any farmer set for himself, for his own success and for his legacy to those who will follow him on the land.

Those able missionaries of soil conservation, Chief Hugh Bennett of the Soil Conservation Service and the patriotic society, Friends of The Land, trenchantly point out that fifty million acres of our lands are gone forever, fifty million more well on the way to unproductivity, and another one hundred million seriously threatened. This national tragedy has been misunderstood by some laymen, however. They have thought that all farmers were wastrels of the basic national substance, soil fertility. They have thought that all farmlands were disappearing and that soon America would be a desert.

Of course, this is not so—although it must be granted that had not the above missionaries tirelessly preached imminent disaster, our future would have been precarious indeed. But in all parts of the country there have always been soil patriots whose greatest desire was to leave their children a farm better than it was when the parents took over.

2. Soil Doctors and Missionaries

THE genesis of mineral soils (that is, all soils except the peats and mucks) is the accumulation of broken and finely divided rock. Yes, even "the everlasting rocks" decompose when exposed long enough to the elements of nature. Heat and cold cause fission. Wind or water grind them one on another and granulate them. The solvent action of chemical-bearing water advances decomposition. The fine particles that result may remain where they developed, or may be picked up by water, ice, or wind, possibly to be mixed with other particles and redeposited in a new location. The earth-mantle thus accumulated is the "parent material" from which soil develops—but it is not soil. It is sterile and inert. It contains little or no life and little of the essential nitrogen in forms useful as plant food. Some coarse-feeding plants will grow on it, though even these grow poorly at first, as they do on freshly exposed subsoil in road cuts or on fields where the fertile topsoil layer has been removed.

Yet plants slowly find roothold; insects and animals work over the material and in it; various bacteria and fungus growths begin to develop. From as far down as their roots penetrate, the plants absorb moisture, along with mineral nutrients from the decomposed rock. These are combined with carbon dioxide from the air to form organic substances—the food alike for plants and for animals. When the plants and the animals die, they fall upon the surface, only to be attacked and decomposed by insects and microscopic forms of life, which, in their turn, multiply and die. Thus, through countless deaths over a period of time too long to have meaning against the brief span of man, organic matter is added to the otherwise sterile mineral debris. A true soil is on the way to development.

The soil may appear inert—just so much rock and organic remains—but nothing could be further from the truth. A fertile soil teems with life. Earthworms and insects are visible to the human eye. Added to them are countless millions of microscopic bacteria and fungus growths. The organic matter of the soil is the basis for this life. It has a significance to the farmer that cannot be overemphasized. Throughout the whole process of its decomposition, nitrogen and mineral nutrients are released in forms readily assimilated by plants. The more there is of organic matter in the soil and the more rapid its decomposition, the more rapidly plants will grow. The soft, dark mold at the grass roots is a ferment of microscopic life, creating plant food in its turn.

For this reason, a high level of organic matter in the soil is desirable at all times. Yet only through its breakdown and loss are its full benefits made available to the farmer. To promote the growth of the microorganisms causing the decomposition, he tills his land, breaking the topsoil finely and mixing in air. His crops

9

grow better, but he has drawn that much more heavily on his "organic-matter bank account." Nature, in her wisdom, returns plant growth to the soil and so maintains the balance. The farmer takes off his crops, in most cases to the detriment of future yields unless in other ways he replaces what his soils gave up.

We in America have an insatiable desire to find a single simple remedy for any problem, no matter how complex. Hence, we are known internationally as faddists who run after any new messiah who promises a painless solution to our difficulties. In the matter of the depletion of soil nutrients through crop removal, there is currently a theory gaining much attention, particularly among laymen, that promises to allay the trouble through "organic gardening."

In brief, the proponents of this school claim that by gathering all crop wastes, composting every organic material on the farm, and applying this manure to the land, they will entirely replace the nutrients lost in crop removal. Sir Albert Howard, the famous English experimenter, has proved to his own satisfaction and that of many thousands of others that the method is feasible and economical, particularly in India and on his own test plots in England. But, while admitting that it may be a perfectly good idea on small plots or where labor is coolie cheap, most agronomists have little faith in the idea from a standpoint of commercial agriculture in America.

A variant of the idea was worked out by a German, Rudolph Steiner, that is called the "bio-dynamic method" of soil treatment. To the compost heap he advocates the addition of a plant preparation which is claimed to act as yeast, speeding and improving the fertilizing qualities of the decomposing materials. The leader of this movement in America is Ehrenfried Pfeiffer of Pennsylvania, who claims several thousand adherents.[1] Again, the theory has not been adapted to commercial agriculture on a wide scale, although very recently a book entitled *Pay Dirt* has attracted much attention and may bring in its wake wide experimentation and possibly an eventual significant acceptance.[2]

Another group professes to rely on the earthworm population

[1] Ehrenfried Pfeiffer, *Bio-Dynamic Farming and Gardening* (New York, Anthroposophic Press, 1938).
[2] J. I. Rodale, *Pay Dirt* (New York, The Devin-Adair Company, 1945).

and the increase thereof to help in maintaining fertility. The theory is that earthworms coming up from the subsoil carry with them the necessary minerals found in the deeper regions. Their castings then fertilize the topsoil. An earthworm farm in Illinois and another in Connecticut offer earthworms commercially for this purpose. However, agriculturists at large have been dilatory about adopting this theory, although many farmers consider a large earthworm population a rule-of-thumb index to soil fertility.

Topping all the popular theorists, at least in the attention he has received, is Edward H. Faulkner, of *Plowman's Folly* fame.[3] His little book enjoyed one of the greatest sales in the entire history of books on farming. In it, the author advocated displacing the plow with the disk or some variant of that tool. Crops of green manure such as rye, he says, should be planted in fall and disked under the following spring. A wheel with spikes placed around its rim then runs over the soil, compressing it and providing a spacer and dibble for planting. The surface trash is left in place. Tremendous yields are claimed for the method, as well as freedom from attacks by the usual pests.

The book aroused a furor of controversy. Agronomists admit that some soils should not be plowed and, further, that improper plowing had caused many troubles. Undoubtedly the book had a beneficial effect on widening the interest in stubble-mulching which Mack Gowder of Georgia has been practicing with success for twenty years. Nevertheless, the plow seems here to stay for a while at least, for there is not yet evidence that the Faulkner theories are applicable on a wide scale, nor to any considerable number of soil types or climatic variations.

The novelist Louis Bromfield has written and spoken to a very wide audience on the Faulkner theory. Bromfield found on his own Malabar Farm in Lucas, Ohio, that the theory worked well on berry bushes, that it did help build topsoil. A story is going the rounds that Bromfield succeeded in building up the topsoil very successfully on one badly depleted field by following Faulkner's theories. On a day when Faulkner was visiting at Malabar, he was horrified to see his enemy, the plow, hard at work turning the ground. When he expostulated, Farmer Bromfield laughed

[3] Norman, University of Oklahoma Press, 1943.

and said, "Sure—the theory worked so well, I'm turning this top-soil under and then I'll grow some more on top again."

In a letter to the authors, Mr. Bromfield updates the story. He says: "Actually the answer is that we do use a plow and plow deeply but instead of turning the furrow completely over and burying the surface manure or rubbish we set the furrow on edge and then chop it up with a heavy disk, incorporating all manure and rubbish into the soil to a depth of 9″. In other words, instead of merely scratching the surface we carry the process down to a depth of 8″ or 9″ and about every three years turn the whole thing over to begin on the bottom. . . . It is not a repudiation of Faulkner but rather out-Faulknering Faulkner."

At the Nebraska station, careful experiments are under way to see if stubble-mulching (leaving the trash on top of the ground) is feasible in the Great Plains area. There the purpose is not so much to replace nutrients as it is to conserve moisture and stop wind erosion. While the experiments are not complete, early evidence seems to indicate that for moisture conservation and erosion-retarding the idea is a good one.

Mr. Faulkner has recently published a new book, *A Second Look*,[4] which amplifies his views and corrects some misconceptions. From it the following illuminating quotes are taken:

"While the book [*Plowman's Folly*] was intended to draw an indictment of the plow, the far more important purpose was to show the reader the need for highly developed biological activity in the soil. If biological activity were not the fundamental consideration, the discussion of the plow's faults would be pointless. . . .

"Nowhere in the book did I say explicitly that the discussion was directed almost wholly toward a single class of farmers: those whose land already had become so unproductive that it could no longer finance, in the conventional way, its own rejuvenation. Failure to indicate this slant in the text caused many people to encounter difficulty when they tried to apply the ideas of the book to land that already was in highly productive condition."[5]

Now that everybody has had a chance to reply to the indict-

4 Norman, University of Oklahoma Press, 1947.
5 Page 6.

ments in *Plowman's Folly,* it is only fair that its author have an opportunity for rebuttal. His sincere self-criticism as evidenced above indicates that the new book may be more valuable than the first. At least, it will deserve a reading by anyone eager to get all points of view on soil management.

There is much scientific evidence available to show that the removal of nutrients by crops is a serious matter and their return of prime importance. A sample is found in the work of Salter, Lewis, and Slipher in Ohio, from whom the following quotations are taken. "J. W. Ames, chemist at the Ohio Agricultural Experiment Station, obtained at several locations samples of comparable virgin and cropped soils; he took a sample of virgin forest or grass land, then climbed the fence and took a comparable sample from cropped land on the same type of soil. These samples were analyzed . . . for the important element nitrogen, which is contained in the soil organic matter.

"Nitrogen forms such a constant part of the organic matter that it serves as a criterion of the amount of organic matter present in the soil. As an average for seven virgin soils in Ohio, there were present 4,214 pounds of nitrogen in one acre of surface soils; whereas the average for comparable cultivated soils was 2,744 pounds, a loss of 1,470 pounds or just about one-third. Most of these cultivated soils had been farmed only for a period of from 50 to 75 years [about the active farming lifetimes of a father-son succession on the land]."[6]

On the Ohio Agricultural Experiment Station farm at Wooster, certain experiments in crop yields have been in progress since before the turn of the century. "From time to time the plots involved in these experiments have been sampled and subjected to chemical analysis. One of the most complete studies has been made on samples taken in 1925. . . . The results of the laboratory studies of these soils, compared to crop yields, indicate a close relationship between changes in the organic matter and nitrogen content of a given type of soil and its capacity to produce. . . . By way of illustration, data from the untreated check plots in an experiment in which corn has been grown continuously since 1894 are presented.

[6] Salter, Lewis, and Slipher, *Our Heritage—the Soil,* 5–6.

13

"Relative Nitrogen Content and Yield of Continuous
Corn Plots at Wooster, Ohio

Year	Relative nitrogen content of soil	Year	Relative Corn Yield
1896	100.0 per cent	1894–1898	100.0
1913	51.6	1911–1915	59.6
1925	41.2	1923–1927	45.6

"With the continuous cropping to corn, the nitrogen content
of the soil has decreased markedly, and simultaneously the yield
of corn has declined almost in proportion. It is believed that this
relationship is sufficiently exact to permit the use of changes in
the nitrogen or organic content of the soil as an approximate
measure of the effect of a cropping system or management practice
upon the productivity of a given type of soil."[7]

Of course, farmers have long known that one crop cannot be
grown year after year on the same unmanured, unfertilized field
without serious detrimental effects on soil productivity. For that
reason these results from continuous cropping to corn might be
regarded as having little significance to actual farming practice.
Further, corn is a particularly destructive crop in its effect on soil
organic matter and nitrogen. The Ohio experiments indicate that
wheat and oats, by contrast, are only about half as destructive,
while hay crops (particularly the legumes) exert a conserving or
cumulative effect. The influence of a long and diversified crop rotation upon soil organic matter is of more interest to farmers than
the result of continuous production of one crop, and fortunately
the Wooster experiments furnish some information on this point—
data, in fact, that farmers may study and digest to their profit.

In 1894, a five-year rotation of corn, oats, wheat, clover, and
timothy was established upon certain plots where the nitrogen
level of the surface soil was determined to be 2,176 pounds per
acre. The rotation was continued without interruption, and the
soil was analyzed in 1925. Lime was applied regularly to the land
after 1900, but no other fertilizers or manure was used. In 1925
the nitrogen content was found to be only 1,546 pounds per acre—
a decrease of 29 per cent in thirty-two years.

The Ohio scientists have not reported the crop yields on this
experiment, but if the decline was in proportion to the depletion

[7] Salter, Lewis, and Slipher, *Our Heritage—the Soil*, 8–9.

of soil nitrogen (as happened to corn yields on the same experimental farm), the rate of decrease was about 1 per cent a year. Here is evidence that soil maintenance is of concern to the farmer now on the land, not merely to those who will follow him. In a normal lifetime of farming, this rotation (commonly considered to be a good one under central Ohio conditions), if the soil were untreated with manure or any fertilizer except lime, would deplete soil productivity one-third—that is, it would do so under soil and climatic conditions similar to those at Wooster. Successful farming cannot be built upon any such short-sighted plan of action.

An analysis of the results of the Wooster experiments and of similar studies on other experimental farms has furnished the basis for Salter, Lewis, and Slipher to assign what they call "indexes" to various crops, that represent approximately the effect of these crops upon soil productivity. "These indexes may be either negative or positive, depending upon whether a particular crop has a soil deteriorating or a soil improving effect. They are conveniently stated as the percentage change in productive capacity of the soil caused by growing each crop for a single year."[8]

Soil Productivity Indexes for Individual Crops in Ohio[9]

Crop	Soil Productivity Index* (per cent change)
Corn	—2.0
Potatoes, tobacco, sugar beets	—2.0
Oats, wheat, barley, rye, buckwheat	—1.0
Soybeans–harvested for hay	—0.5
–seed harvested, straw and leaves left in field	0.0
Timothy and other grass sods	0.0
Red and alsike clovers	+2.0
Alfalfa (1 year)	+2.5
Alfalfa (2 years or more)	+3.0 (total)
Sweet clover for green manure	+2.5
Mixed meadows	* *
Rotation pastures	* *

* These indexes have to be modified for applications of manure or fertilizer, and for the destructive effects of any erosion that may occur.

** A weighted index is calculated for these crops based upon the percentage of different plants in the herbage.

8 Salter, Lewis, and Slipher, *Our Heritage—the Soil,* 10.

9 Salter, Lewis, and Slipher, *Our Heritage—the Soil,* 11.

Intertilled crops such as corn, potatoes, and tobacco—unfertilized and unmanured—are all given a factor of minus 2 per cent, indicating that each time one of these crops is grown there is a loss of about 2 per cent in the productive capacity of the soil. A crop of clover, on the other hand, with a plus factor of 2 per cent, is considered to offset the effect of one crop of corn.

How would these figures check out for a rotation? For five years of corn, oats, wheat, clover, and timothy, the indexes would be −2.0, −1.0, −1.0, +2.0, 0.0; a net decrease in soil productivity of minus 2 per cent. For five years of corn, oats, alfalfa, alfalfa, alfalfa, they would be −2.0, −1.0, +3.0; no net change. The degree to which these weightings of individual crops have checked out with changes in soil organic matter and crop yields indicate that, with the soil and climatic conditions that prevail at Wooster, they are just about right.

Farmers using manure or commercial fertilizer or both are adding to the productivity of their soils, and the indexes must be adjusted accordingly. The evidence in Ohio is that each ton of manure adds 0.125 per cent, and each 200 pounds of "average" commercial fertilizer adds the same. Thus a corn, corn, oats, clover rotation that, according to the indexes, would deplete soil productivity 3 per cent could be balanced with 4,800 pounds of "average" fertilizer or 24 tons of manure or proportionate shares of each.

These index values might be considered as particularly applicable to the eastern Corn Belt and of most value to the farmers of that region.[10] Surely on different soils, and particularly under different climatic conditions than prevail at Wooster, they would have to be modified. But it is equally certain that Salter and his associates have established a highly important principle. *The influence of a cropping plan upon soil productivity can be measured, and farmers can adjust their soil maintenance programs to it.*

Similar information is needed for other parts of the country where soils and climate differ materially from those of Ohio, where other crops are grown, and where manure and commercial fertilizers are used in different quantity and proportion. Until such information is more complete, farmers will have to adjust these indexes to suit their own conditions.

Soil may be compared to a cold-blooded animal. When we speak of it as a living body, we mean, of course, that it contains living organisms that most definitely make the soil "an active body."[11] The life within the soil is of cold-blooded forms. Their rate of activity is in proportion to temperature and the amount of moisture and air. They lie relatively dormant in the cold of winter, particularly if the soil is frozen, only to revive with the return of moist, warm weather in the spring. For each eighteen degrees Fahrenheit rise in temperature (assuming moisture and oxygen supplies are adequate), their rate of activity approximately doubles, and the plant nutrients that they digest and then release to growing crops rise in proportion. Thus, in climates warmer and more moist than in Ohio, the depletion of soil organic matter is more rapid, and a high level in the soil is more difficult to maintain. In cooler and drier climates, the rate of decomposition is slower. The crop indexes that fit conditions at Wooster must be adjusted accordingly.

Intertilled crops that are cultivated regularly, so that a greater supply of oxygen is mixed into the surface soil where the soil organisms are concentrated, bring about a greater decomposition and depletion of organic matter than crops not cultivated after planting. Of course, a large crop has a greater influence upon fertility than a small crop. A one hundred-bushel corn crop takes more from the soil than a fifty-bushel crop, and three tons of clover per acre returns more nitrogen than a one-ton yield. Again, the indexes must be adjusted accordingly.

The Ohio scientists estimate that with the crops now grown in their state and the inadequate soil-maintenance programs now followed, the soil productivity of Ohio is declining six-tenths of 1 per cent each year. If this rate is continued over the next fifty years, the result will be a one-quarter decrease in soil productivity and a roughly comparable decrease in crop yields. Ohio is not alone in this trend. Probably few states are doing better, and surely many states are not doing so well.

Yet, as an individual engaged in the business of farming, the farmer needs to be concerned with what is happening on his farm.

[10] For a similar study in Missouri, see A. W. Kleeme and O. T. Coleman, *Evaluating Annual Changes in Soil Productivity* (Missouri Agricultural Experiment Station Bulletin 405, 1939).

[11] See also William A. Albrecht, "The Soil—An Active Body," *The Philfarmer* (First and Second Quarters, 1945), 2.

The overall national picture is a matter of public policy, and a vital one indeed. But Salter and his associates, together with many other soil scientists, have shown us that soils can be maintained—depletion is not inevitable.

3. Humus

THE function of organic matter in the soil does not end with making available the nitrogen and other plant nutrients released by decomposition. "It's a pleasure to cultivate corn after clover," said a young farmer in DeKalb County, Illinois. "But corn that follows corn means a lot of trouble with stubble that plugs the cultivator teeth, and the soil is lots harder." He operated a farm with his father on which corn, corn, oats, and clover was the established rotation. He was expressing a problem that has bothered many a thoughtful farmer. With continued production of intensively tilled row crops, soil becomes less friable, clods more easily, is more difficult to reduce to a good seedbed, and likewise more difficult to cultivate. On this particular farm, with considerable livestock and consequently manure to go back on the land, soil productivity is being maintained; average crop yields are increasing. But the tilth of the soil deteriorated enough from the first to the second crop of corn in rotation to be disturbing to this observant young farmer.

In the early stages of decomposition, some fragments of organic materials returned to the soil will retain recognizable form. A more advanced stage of breakdown, however, results in a residue known as humus. Chemically it is highly complex, consisting of many different compounds formed during the decomposition process. Physically it is amorphous and dark colored, with a pleasant odor.

Humus is more stable than fresh organic matter in the soil—that is, its final breakdown takes place more slowly; yet in no sense is it a permanent material. It may be thought of as the final stage in the return of chemically complex organic matter into the elements and chemically simple compounds of the mineral kingdom. Its ultimate breakdown releases the final units of plant food contained in the organic tissues from which it came.

But the function of humus in the soil is far more than just the release of the plant nutrients it carries. It modifies such important physical properties of the soil as structure, friability, and moisture-holding capacity. Humus is a veritable sponge in its ability to hold moisture, soaking up large amounts in wet periods and making it available to plants later, when they might otherwise suffer from drought. The amount of water required by growing plants is almost unbelievably great. The production of enough wheat for one loaf of bread requires about one ton. An acre of corn yielding fifteen tons of corn silage requires 1,800 tons of water from planting time to harvest—an amount equal to sixteen inches of rain falling at the proper time and all utilized by the corn.

Crops far more commonly suffer from a lack of moisture than from an excess, but they suffer much less on land with a high humus content because the humus acts as a regulator of the supply. In a dry summer a few years ago we saw a tomato field in the Lake region, on part of which a heavy crop of green manure had been raised the year before. The other part of the field had been used for intertilled row crops for two years with no organic matter added. The difference in the size and condition of the tomato plants on the two parts of the field was striking. Where the green manure had been plowed down, they covered the ground completely and were heavily set with fruit. When the plants were moved aside, the soil under them was found to be soft and moist. On the other side of the field the plants were smaller and carried less fruit. The soil was harder and obviously drier. A considerable number of fruits were developing a black, blossom-end rot—a physiological condition resulting from moisture deficiency. The value of green manure may not usually be so strikingly apparent, but here the organic matter it added was carrying a crop successfully through a dry period that was ruining the same crop on a part of the same field where the humus content of the soil was lower.

The moisture-holding capacity of humus is of maximum value on light sandy or sandy loam soils. Soils such as these retain little water if the humus content is low, and crops suffer accordingly much more than on silts or clays. But humus is a versatile substance. On heavy silt and clay soils, where its significance in moisture relations is somewhat less than on light soils, it contributes another valuable function. It promotes granulation, a bringing together in granule form of many tiny soil particles, converting an otherwise hard, lumpy soil into one far more soft, friable, easy to fit and to cultivate; more porous and absorptive of rainfall and consequently less subject to erosion; better aerated and thus more favorable to the rapid development of soil organisms and plant roots. Clay soils, particularly, have the reputation of being difficult to work. One day they are too wet and spongy; the next day, too dry and hard. A condition of this nature can be immensely improved with addition of organic matter in quantities that will result in the accumulation of a high humus content.

Another quotation from Ohio Bulletin 175 is pertinent to this point: "Associated with [the loss of organic matter] is often found a deterioration in the tilth of a soil, particularly on the heavier types of land. For some time, farmers on the heavier clay and silty clay loam soils of north-western Ohio have been telling us that their land is getting heavier, that it doesn't drain so well as it once did, that it is more difficult to work down into a good seed-bed, that it cracks worse in dry weather, and that satisfactory legume seedings are more difficult to obtain. All of these happenings indicate that these soils are losing their granular structure and becoming more compact and impervious.

"Our soil physicist, Richard Bradfield, started in 1935 to see if any evidence existed that such changes are actually taking place. In Paulding County, he sampled several comparable pairs of virgin and cropped soils, taking these samples at successive one foot depths down to three or four feet. Among other things, he determined the weight of a cubic foot of each of these samples. In the field a given volume of soil is made up partly of solid soil material and partly of pore space filled with air and water. Obviously, the more a soil weighs per cubic foot, the greater the volume occupied by solid material, the less the amount of pore space through which air and water can move, and the harder it will be for roots to penetrate.

"A part of what Dr. Bradfield found in answer to the farmers' statements is shown for a typical Paulding County silty clay loam.

"The virgin soil was grass land that had been plowed for the first time and put into corn. The cultivated land was of the same soil type, just across the fence, and had been cropped for 40 years, mostly to corn and oats. This field was also in corn. The soil of the virgin field was so loose one could scoop it up with his hands; that of the cultivated field, so hard one could scarcely dent it with his heel. On the virgin field, the corn was expected to yield 75 to 80 bushels per acre, but 20 bushels was about the expectation for the previously cultivated field.

Effects of 40 Years' Croppings on Physical Properties of
Nappanee Silty Clay Loam in Paulding County, Ohio

Depth	Weight of soil per cubic foot		Pore space as per cent of total volume	
	virgin	cultivated	virgin	cultivated
FEET	POUNDS	POUNDS	PER CENT	PER CENT
0–1	65.5	81.7	60.3	50.5
1–2	70.3	86.7	58.1	47.6
2–3	76.6	91.0	53.5	44.8

". . . For each foot of depth, the soil of the cultivated field was much heavier than at a corresponding depth in the virgin soil. In the upper 3 feet there was 16 pounds more of solid soil material in each cubic foot of volume. The cultivated soil contained only about four-fifths as much pore space as the virgin soil. This loss is of the larger pores through which soil air and water move most readily."[1]

Obviously a decline in soil organic matter is a serious form of soil depletion, yet one that is taking place on many farms (possibly a majority) at a rate far too rapid to bode well for the continued success of those farms as going businesses. Such losses are decreasing soil productivity both in available plant nutrients and in a desirable physical condition of the soil. A farmer may "skin his land," but to what avail if its future productivity is reduced? Farming is a long-time business. Those who would get rich quick should find other fields for their talents; it is seldom possible in farming. Successful farming is based upon continuing the capacity of the soil to produce good yields. More and more is the level of soil productivity coming to be recognized in land values; less and less will it pay to skin the land, then look for a sucker to buy it. Maintaining and enhancing the soil's basic value becomes profitable whether one sells or continues to farm.

1 Pages 6–7.

4. Minerals and Manures

A plan of soil management, directed toward maintaining if not, indeed, gradually improving the productivity of the soil, is a vital part of the business management of a farm. It bears exactly the same relation to successful farming that factory maintenance bears to the continued success of a manufacturing business. Good soil-management planning is conditioned to the needs of the individual farm on which it is a part of the plan of operation.

No one farmer will grow everything listed in the seed catalogs—at least if he is a commercial farmer, he will not long continue to do so. He will devote his land and "sell" his labor to some particular type of farming that offers reasonable opportunity for success.

The climate of his area, certain characteristics of his soils that could not easily be changed, and comparative opportunities to market different types of produce will be among the influences determining his selection of crops. Around the rotation thus determined, he will build his business; and to his own cropping plan his program of soil maintenance must be adjusted.

Should the crops be fed to livestock, producing manure to go back on the land, the program will differ from one adjusted to cash cropping; i.e., a fruit orchard may demand different soil treatment than potatoes; a truck gardener may need a different program still. In any event, the plan must be adapted to the soil on the individual farm and to the crops that are to be grown.

Proper nutrition of plants is fully as essential to successful crop farming as proper animal nutrition is to the stockman. In fact, the two may be closely related. Livestock (yes, and humans) eat the crops; and starved plants mean animals that have "a hidden hunger" for certain essential food elements. However, our immediate concern is with plants, and their proper growth is dependent upon a balance of available nutrient materials in the soil that will furnish all the various nutrients that are needed, in the proper proportions.

Much attention has already been given to organic matter, and properly so, because among its other values it is the main source of nitrogen to most crop plants. If any one nutrient can be

22

said to be the most important in crop production, that one is nitrogen. But only because nitrogen is often a limiting factor on land that has long been farmed and abused, can even this nutrient be called the most important. Plants must have many nutrients—including carbon, oxygen, nitrogen, calcium, potassium, phosphorous, magnesium, sulfur, boron, copper, manganese, zinc, and iron—and are limited in their growth by the lack or inadequacy of any one.

Two of these elements, carbon and oxygen, are obtained directly from the air. Others are needed in such minute quantities or are usually available in the soil in such large quantities as to cause little concern to the farmer. Only four—calcium, nitrogen, phosphorous, and potassium—are frequently required by crop plants in excess of the supply, and thus are commonly limiting factors in crop growth. It is these four to which the agricultural-fertilizer industry gives primary attention; it is these four that determine frequently the plus or minus of farm income.

All of the mineral elements naturally present in the soil are made available through the decomposition of the rocks in which they were originally carried. In the early days of soil studies, the belief was widely held that the soil was a "storage bin," containing plant nutrients in certain determinable amounts. It was believed that the soil could be analyzed to determine its content of plant nutrients, and as these were taken from the soil by cropping, they could be returned in the same quantities by plant residues, manures, and fertilizers, and the soil would be kept as it was. Probably Baron Justus von Liebig of Germany, the "Father of Agricultural Chemistry," was more responsible for this early belief than any other man. "The crops on a field diminish or increase in exact proportion to the diminution or increase in mineral substances conveyed to it in manure," he said.

The storage-bin concept has now been discarded. It is recognized that plant nutrients may be lost from the soil by other means than removal by plants. Some may leach away in drainage water in the humid parts of the country. Some may be lost from sloping lands by erosion. And new nutrients may also become available in the soil through further decomposition of soil materials. No longer is soil considered static; it is now recognized for what it is, dynamic and ever changing.

This knowledge, however, has done little to change the complexity of soil-fertility problems, particularly as related to the use of chemical fertilizers. More is involved in proper plant nutrition than dumping fertilizer from a bag. Soils may have a sufficiency of mineral elements and still be unproductive. Soils that analyze "rich" may still give poor yields.

In addition to the other functions of organic matter, it is highly important in releasing mineral elements into forms usable by plants. "Organic matter may well be considered as fuel for bacterial fires in the soil, which operates as a factory producing plant nutrients," says Professor William A. Albrecht of the University of Missouri. "The organic matter is burned to carbon dioxide, ash, and other residues. This provides carbonic acid in the soil water, and the solvent effect of this acidified water on calcium, potassium, magnesium, phosphates, and other minerals in rock form is many hundreds of times greater than that of rainwater. At the same time the complex constituents of organic matter are simplified, and nitrogen . . . is released. . . .

"Decomposition by microorganisms within the soil is the reverse of the process represented by plant growth above the soil. Growing plants, using the energy of the sun, synthesize carbon, nitrogen, and all other elements into complex compounds. The energy stored up in these compounds is then used . . . by the microorganisms whose activity within the soil makes nutrients available for a new generation of plants. Organic matter thus supplies the 'life of the soil' in the strictest sense.

"When measured in terms of carbon dioxide output, the soil is a live, active body. An acre of the better Corn Belt soils in Iowa or northern Illinois, for example, exhales more than 25 times as much of this gas per day as does an adult man at work. Such a soil area burns carbon at a rate equivalent to 1.6 pounds of a good grade of soft coal per hour. The heat equivalent evolved in the same time would convert more than 17 pounds of water to steam under 100 pounds of pressure. A 40-acre corn field during the warmer portion of a July day is burning organic matter in the soil with an energy output equivalent to that of a 40-horsepower steam engine; every acre, in other words, may be roughly pictured as a factory using the equivalent of one horsepower. Organic matter is the source of the power without which the plant-food elements could not be changed into usable forms."[1]

Thus the "burning" of organic matter supplies, in addition to nitrogen, mineral elements, both from amounts carried and from insoluble, useless forms in rock minerals. But if a soil is poorly drained, or poorly aerated, or excessively dry, so that bacterial "fires" burn slowly, it may be unproductive though it assays rich. Its infertility lies in the fact that its nutrients are "locked up" and are practically unavailable to plants. Many a piece of unproductive land has been drained and cultivated, or has been supplied with irrigation water, and thereby been converted into high productivity merely by creating a favorable environment for the bacterial production of plant nutrients.

Fertilizers applied to such land are often a wasted expense until the more limiting factors for plant growth are eliminated. Corrective soil measures such as drainage and irrigation are expensive. One needs to be sure beyond reasonable doubt that the soil treatment will justify the expense before cold cash is laid out to correct "nature's mistakes."

Nor are the soil deficiencies already listed the only ones limiting the value and usefulness of fertilizers on the farm. Soil acidity is another handicap of major proportions over much of the eastern United States. Reference has already been made to the production of carbonic acid in the soil. Nitric and sulfuric acids are similarly produced. It is through the reaction of these acids with the minerals of the soil that nutrients are made available to plants. In humid regions the plants may be "cheated." Excess water percolating down through the soil may leach nutrients to below their reach, if not actually all the way through the soil profile and into the drainage water that goes to feed streams and springs.

Calcium, present in the soil in limestone, is one of the more active minerals reacting with soil acids. Where leaching is sufficient to gradually but steadily reduce the supplies of calcium and related minerals in the soil, the acid-alkaline balance (that favorite phrase of hypochondriac-creating radio advertisers) is upset. Soil acidity increases, with many detrimental effects upon plant growth and nutrition.

[1] "Loss of Soil Organic Matter and Its Restoration," *Soils and Men* (U. S. D. A. Yearbook, 1938), 348–49.

Across the United States from the eastern seaboard and Gulf coast to the sunset shadow of the Sierra Nevadas, annual rainfall gradually decreases, to rise again in the Pacific Northwest. The heavier the rainfall, the more serious are soil losses through leaching. Throughout the East and the South, soil acidity is a limiting factor in fertility, except in local areas where limestone materials are unusually plentiful in the soil.

Soil acidity is a matter of degree, which the chemist measures on the pH scale. The chemical explanation of pH is complex and unnecessary to this discussion. However, let us point out that a soil testing pH 7 is neither acid nor alkaline but chemically neutral. A pH value below 7 indicates acidity; above 7, alkalinity.[2]

Alkaline range		8.0
		7.5
Neutral		7.0
	Slight acidity	6.5
	Moderate acidity	6.0
		5.5
Acid range	Strong acidity	5.0
	Very strong acidity	4.5
		4.0

pH Scale

In some parts of the semiarid West, alkalinity (alkali soil) is a handicap to successful farming. But for the country as a whole, soil acidity is much more serious. The great majority of farm crops grow best in soils with pH values between 6 and 7, and within this approximate range the most beneficial types of soil bacteria are also most active. Yet large areas in the humid East and South have soils more acid than this optimum—a condition requiring correction by the use of lime before the beneficial effects of other fertilizers may be fully realized in crop response. Applications of nitrates, phosphates, and potash are often of little value against the limitations imposed upon crop growth by strong acidity of the soil.

Agricultural lime is a soil conditioner first and a crop fertilizer

[2] The chart given is adapted from Earl Jones, *Liming Ohio Soils* (Ohio State University Extension Bulletin 177, 1936), 8.

second. It is widely used by farmers for correcting acidity, but not widely enough. Reducing soil acidity will stimulate the activity of the most desirable kinds of soil bacteria, will "unlock" other mineral elements now present in the soil but not available to plants, and will make it possible to grow good crops of clovers and other legumes on soils where these crops now fail. Legume crops (principally the clovers and alfalfa)—the most valuable of all in maintaining and increasing the productivity levels of cultivated land— require a fair abundance of lime in the soil.

Salter and his associates in Ohio state: "A summary of several thousand soil tests indicates that two-thirds of the cropped land of Ohio is too acid to produce satisfactory clover and only one-fourth is in shape to grow either alfalfa or sweet clover well. Moreover, the soils of the state are becoming increasingly acid, since the amount of lime used[3] is estimated to be less than one-fifth that needed to maintain their soils at their present reaction status. It is estimated that to put the cropped land of Ohio in condition to grow red clover and alfalfa within a 25-year period, and at the same time compensate for annual losses of lime through crops and drainage, would require the yearly application of around 2,000,000 tons of limestone."[4]

Many states east and south of Ohio have an equal if not still more serious problem of soil acidity. Many farmers in states to the west cannot afford to ignore the problem.

How much lime do you need? Which of the several kinds should you buy? It depends upon your soil, how much you wish to reduce acidity, and your crop rotation. (Note that some types of mineral fertilizers definitely increase the acidity of the soil. Several years' use of fertilizers of this sort, plus leaching, more than likely will make liming a profitable operation even where it was not necessary before.)

To the question when lime should be applied, Dr. Carl Bender of the New Jersey Experiment Station has a favorite reply. He

[3] The peak tonnage up to 1936 when this bulletin was written was 233,000 tons in 1929. It has since increased, reaching about 1,250,000 tons in 1943.

[4] Salter, Lewis, and Slipher, *Our Heritage—the Soil*, 13.

27

says, "All days of the year except fifty-two. You shouldn't work on Sundays."

A highly valuable service furnished by county agricultural agents is to test soils for acidity and make recommendations that fit the circumstances. But heed the evidence. Correct your pH first. Other fertilizers may profitably follow. Here the recommendations of your state agricultural experiment station for your soil, your crops, and your locality are a reliable guide.

In the humid parts of the country, and in some soils in other areas, phosphates are deficient for maximum crop growth. (A notable exception is in the Bluegrass region of Kentucky and Tennessee). Phosphates are frequently "unlocked" and the deficiency at least partly corrected by reducing soil acidity. But this nutrient is so highly important both to crop yield and crop quality, and is so commonly deficient, especially on eroded land, that you may still need phosphate fertilizer. Your experiment station will tell you.

Nitrogen and potash (potassium) are returned to the land in manure. Nevertheless, even manure, valuable as it is in soil maintenance, will need fortifying with phosphate. With ample manure you may not need to buy nitrogen or potash in chemical form. For some soils and some crops you will; if you lack manure and if you farm in the humid parts of the country, you probably will. Again, your experiment station will tell you.

Much attention has been given in recent years to green-manure crops. These are crops grown for the express purpose of plowing them back into the land. They increase the supply of organic matter in the soil, with all the beneficial effects such treatment brings. Manure accomplishes the same results. Isaac Phillips Roberts, first dean of agriculture at Cornell, once said: "Grow the biggest crop of green manure you can. Harvest it. Feed it to livestock, and put the manure back on the land."

The plant nutrients in manure vary with the kind of animal, the kinds and proportions of feed that animal received, the proportions of liquid and solid excreta that are salvaged, and the degree to which the manure is exposed to weathering before being applied to the land. Handled in a manner to avoid losses, it returns to the land nearly half of the organic matter, three-quarters of the nitrogen and phosphorous, and seven-eighths of the potassium that was contained in the original feed.[5]

To follow Professor Roberts' advice is good management for the farmer who keeps livestock. He may return these proportions of the plant nutrients in the feed to the land, and he has the livestock production that the feed made possible in addition. On Seabrook Farms, biggest vegetable farm in the world, a large herd of beef cattle is kept primarily for the manure the animals make rather than for the profit on the cattle. Where dairy cattle are kept, superphosphate sprinkled in the gutters will control barn odors, aid in fly retarding, and have a very definite value in preserving all plant nutrients in the manure, particularly slowing up nitrogen loss. For the farmer without livestock, green manure is a "must." Even the livestock man, if he has a truck-crop program, often finds green manure the cheapest form of needed additional fertilizer.

Many truck-crop (and other cash-crop) farmers have been able to do a fair job of soil maintenance by using green manures and chemical fertilizers, even though they raise cultivated row crops on their land nearly every year. However, to do so requires exceedingly careful management. The green-manure crop should be seeded as early as possible after the cash crop is off, so that it may make maximum growth before the winter sets in. It is common practice in some sections to seed in the row after the last cultivation. Crops that grow well in cool fall weather should be used. And legumes, because of their higher nitrogen-producing capacity, should be favored whenever possible.

"From the standpoint of maintaining the organic matter of the soil, bulk is of first importance, and this can often be supplied more efficiently by such a crop as rye, sorghum, or mustard than by a legume. A crop of a non-legume supplies a large amount of energy material, but it must not be forgotten that the bacteria responsible for the decay of this material must have access to nitrogen. If the nitrogen carried in the green manure crop is not sufficient, the bacteria will draw on available soil nitrogen and may deplete it to such an extent as to ruin the following crop. It is not uncommon to find that turning under a nearly ripe crop of rye has been a detriment to the next crop. A legume crop, on the other

[5] E. L. Worthen, *Farm Soils* (New York, John Wiley and Sons, Inc., 1935, 2nd edition), 199–205.

hand, carries with it more than enough nitrogen for its decay and this excess becomes available to the following crop."[6]

Where a nonlegume green manure may result in the maximum production of bulk, one may grow the crop and then apply nitrogen-carrying fertilizer for use by the soil bacteria in carrying out its decomposition. Thus the maximum of organic matter may be returned to the soil without detrimental effects upon the crop that follows.

Professor Firman Bear, Rutgers, widely recognized soil authority, states: "An . . . effective method of procedure is that of growing a heavy sod or a mature cover crop, treating it with nitrogen, and plowing it under. Organic material having a dry weight of 5 tons per acre, treated with 100 pounds of nitrogen and the necessary lime and plowed under will produce about the same effect as an application of 10 tons of manure. It remains to be determined whether anything would be gained by applying a complete fertilizer, instead of nitrogen only, in advance of plowing. Possibly the phosphoric acid and potash can be used to better advantage, if saved for application along the row at planting time."[7]

Recently, some attention has been turned to the possible residual effect of complete fertilizers on green-manure crops and vice versa. A fertilizer program, carefully worked out, should take into consideration these values, particularly where heavy fertilization is recommended for the cash crop in the rotation. In a grassland program where amounts as high as five hundred pounds annually of, say, a 10–10–10 fertilizer are the rule, perhaps no fertilizer at all would be the most economic usage when a green-manure crop comes in the rotation.

Of all the soil-improving materials used by American farmers, farm manure is the one of greatest value. Farmers may profit greatly from giving it more attention, not less. Its story is well told by Salter and Schollenberger: "The crop nutrients [contained in one billion tons of farm manure produced annually on American

[6] A. J. Pieters and Roland McKee, "The Use of Cover and Green Manure," *Soils and Men*, 433–34.

[7] Reprinted by permission from *Theory and Practice in the Use of Fertilizers* (New York, John Wiley and Sons, Inc., 1938, 2nd edition), 321.

On the highly erodible fields of Bernalillo County, New Mexico, contouring makes every furrow a block against washing and a reservoir of always needed moisture.

In Nebraska, where both wind and water erosion are constant threats, basin listing almost completely stops run-off, retards blowing, and builds subsurface moisture supplies.

farms] would cost more than six times as much as was expended for commercial fertilizers in 1936. Its organic matter content is double the amount of soil humus annually destroyed in growing the Nation's grain and cotton crops.

"Unfortunately, only a small fraction of the potential crop-producing and soil-conserving value of manure is actually realized. Probably one-half of the excrements from farm stock is dropped on pastures and uncultivated ground. From the part handled as manure, there are enormous losses through failure to save the valuable liquid portion, through loss of nitrogen in improper fermentation and drying, and through leaching of the remaining available nutrients from storage piles exposed to heavy rainfall. Even after it is spread upon the field, serious losses from volatilization of ammonia are probable if fermented manure dries before it is effectively incorporated into the soil, or at least before the soluble constituents have been leached out and absorbed by the soil. As a final factor in the inefficient use of manure, it is not always applied at the season, in the manner, at the rate, or to the crop which would give the greatest return. Considering these facts, it is probably safe to assume that only a quarter or a third of the potential value of the manure resource of the country is now realized.

"The economic possibility of preventing much of this loss has been conclusively demonstrated, both experimentally and practically. The wasteful and inefficient methods of handling manure seen in all sections are evidence that many farmers still do not understand the true nature of manure, the perishable character of its most valuable constituents, and the direct money loss incurred through its improper treatment. A study of the facts regarding the production, losses, care, and field management of manure should help any farmer better to understand the problem and work out a solution practical for the conditions of his own farm.

"Results obtained at a number of American experiment stations indicate that at present crop prices (1938) the average value of manure as fertilizer is $2.50 per ton.[8] This figure will vary with

[8] This is, of course, the value of the manure applied to the field. Farm cost accounts in New York state indicate that the cost of applying manure is about $0.75 to $1.25 a ton, depending upon the methods by which it is handled. These costs must be considered in valuing manure in the stables or barnyards.

soil and crop—the range of estimates is from $0.96 to $4.11 for general crops in Indiana and about the same in Iowa. The average for 36 tests in Maryland was $5.28, and on truck crops only, $8.67. Assuming an average value of $2.50 and that two-thirds of the potential manure production from feeding all crops except wheat grain is recovered, the annual value of the manure from 100 acres of land producing 50 bushels of corn, 40 bushels of oats, 25 bushels of wheat, and 2 tons of hay per acre in rotation would be $500. By better handling and the use of fertilizer supplements this value might be materially increased.

"The greatest benefits from manure are only to be realized from intelligent use in combination with other practices that constitute good soil management—proper crop rotation, lime if needed, supplemental fertilization, adequate drainage, high-quality seed, and good-tillage practices."[9]

When the American farmer learns to have some of the veneration for the manure pile that his French colleague has, our total agricultural picture will be brightened immeasurably. In France the manure pile in the front yard is almost as sacredly maintained as the roadside shrines. No waste, animal or vegetable, on the farm is allowed to escape that pile. Perhaps, to the French *paysan* the Germans committed no greater atrocity than to drive off the livestock and with it the source of manure. The stable agriculture, the solidity of peasant society, and the peacetime ability of France to be nearly self-sufficient in food is that manure pile.

In many localities here in America, manure is still considered a nuisance. In others, it is something to spread around the barn, as near at hand as convenient. The soil it falls on promptly testifies in green verdure to the values it imparts. But some heedless farmers still think it more trouble than it is worth, even though their yields decline year after year.

In other communities, though, the manure is carefully covered with superphosphate, hauled into covered pits, and cared for as a major profit-maker. The liquid part of the manure is gathered from paved feed floors and preserved. One of the new fertilizing machines that will undoubtedly enjoy a good sale is a liquid ma-

[9] Robert M. Salter and C. J. Schollenberger, "Farm Manure," *Soils and Men*, 445–46.

nure spreader that pumps the material from the pit to portable
tank and provides a distributor system.

Obviously, soil management cannot be tied to farm manure,
green manure, lime, or other fertilizer elements alone. The soil
must be handled physically in the best manner demanded by its
particular consistency. Topographic features must be evaluated
and plans changed accordingly. Conservation is a major item, while
average annual precipitation must condition all other elements.
True, this makes a complex problem, but all aspects of successful
commercial farming are complex. That is just one reason why
farming is no longer (if it ever was) the place for the fellow not
smart enough to be successful at anything else.

Soils are individuals. They must be studied and understood
as individuals. Nothing short of careful and continual study with
this fact in mind will lead to successful management.

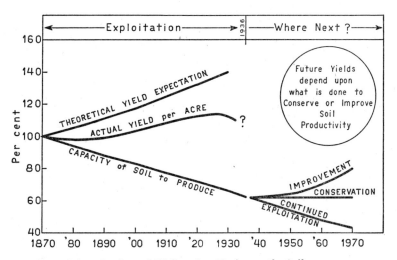

From Salter, Lewis, and Slipher, *Our Heritage—the Soil,* 7.

Improved farming techniques have thus far counterbalanced the
decline in soil productivity. With continued soil exploitation, acre
yields must soon trend downward. Yields can be maintained only if
soil conservation is practiced; they can be increased only if soil-im-
provement practices are adopted and conscientiously followed.

33

5. Water: Friend or Foe?

THE big dairy barn and comfortable farmhouse nestle in a green and fertile valley. Some of the cropland of the farm stretches out across the valley floor, but it is not enough to balance the large acreage of hillside pasture above and behind the buildings.

Two fields on the hillside are used for crops, sufficiently supplementing the crop fields in the valley to enable the farm to produce winter forage for forty cows, and still leave ample pasture. Those two fields are on a 12 per cent slope; that is, twelve feet of rise for every one hundred feet of horizontal distance. For many years a fence has stood across the hillside, dividing the upper field from the lower. Another, close to the base of the hill, separates the lower field from the farmstead.

In the course of the years some soil from that slope has answered the call of gravity, has been washed downhill, or at least part way down, to be checked by the two fence rows. Along each one enough soil has accumulated to build up a moderate terrace, so that now the fences are a foot or so higher on the lower side than on the upper.

In spite of the fact that about thirty inches of rain fall on that hillside each year between spring thaws and the winter freeze-up, those fields could in no sense be called seriously eroded. The topsoil is still thick; good crop yields are produced. Only where water has accumulated in the wheel ruts of a driveway running at a steep angle down the hill has any serious washing occurred. The driveway has, in fact, become something of a gully, though not enough to make it unusable. Thousands of hillsides, yes, hundreds of thousands—less steep than this one and receiving less rainfall, have been seriously eroded, even to the point of destroying them for farming.

"Erosion is as old as agriculture," says Dr. Hugh H. Bennett, chief of the Soil Conservation Service. "It began when the first heavy rain struck the first furrow turned by a crude implement of tillage in the hands of prehistoric man. It has been going on ever since, wherever man's culture of the earth has bared the soil to rain and wind."

34

Many persons who are in a position to know regard erosion as the outstanding soil-depleting force at work in America. One is prone to agree when he has seen sloping crop fields washed clean of fertile topsoil, or the gullies that are all too common in the Piedmont of the Southeast and on the rolling clay uplands of the South, or some of the fertile silts of the Corn Belt melted away like sugar in flowing water from very moderate slopes indeed; or when, along the hundredth meridian, he has seen the sun blacked out by howling storms of dust.

A soil-erosion survey made in the United States a decade ago indicated that from one-half to all the topsoil was then eroded from one hundred million acres of cropland. (That is, it all had been cropland. Much of it no longer supported profitable farming.)

While in the semiarid parts of the country wind erosion may be destructive, particularly to bare fields in dry years, for the country as a whole water erosion does far more damage. In humid areas, agriculture is more concentrated; each farmer operates a smaller acreage and is more dependent upon each acre.

Bennett and Lowdermilk estimate that fully 75 per cent of the land surface of the country slopes sufficiently to discharge water at an erosive rate. Their estimate is based upon the fact that "every known measurement at erosion experiment stations throughout the country shows some loss of both soil and water on unprotected slopes of 2 per cent or more."[1]

Obviously, the steeper the slope, the more rapidly water will run off, the higher will be the proportion of total rainfall that does run off, and the more serious will be the erosion problem unless steps are taken to check it. A 2 per cent slope is very moderate; a 12 per cent slope such as is being cropped on the dairy farm previously described is a "right smart" grade from which water will run off with much greater velocity.

"Doubling the speed or velocity of running water makes it four times as effective in scouring the soil surface and in loosening particles that are then carried away. If the velocity is increased three times, the scouring ability is made nine times greater.

[1] Hugh H. Bennett and W. C. Lowdermilk, "General Aspects of the Erosion Problem," *Soils and Men*, 591 n.

35

"The carrying power of water, that is, the weight of the separate particles that water is capable of carrying in suspension, is increased more by increased velocity than is the scouring power of running water. Doubling the velocity of a stream increases carrying power 64 times; trebling the velocity increases carrying power to the almost unbelievable extent of 729 times."[2]

Why then, in view of these facts, have not the hillside crop fields on that dairy farm been much more seriously eroded? There is more than one answer, of course; but the most important is that they are used primarily as hay meadows. The soil is fertilized and manured, the sod is dense, and that sod is an erosion-controlling agent of the first order. About six years in eight those fields are down to hay. When they are plowed up, it is to grow corn for ensilage, to be followed by oats with which a new hay seeding is established. The corn rows are planted across the slope, not up and down it, a scheme which further checks erosion. But even so, it is in the years when corn is grown that most of the erosion on those fields takes place.

"The aim in erosion control is to make water 'walk off' from sloping land rather than to 'run off,' " is a statement attributed to former Secretary of Agriculture Henry A. Wallace. Excellent as this statement is, it neglects to stress that the most desirable situation is to aim to make the water soak in, with only the minimum of runoff.

Soil erosion of the kind that depletes farmland (or that, unchecked, may actually destroy it) should not be confused with geological erosion that has been going on in the natural environment undisturbed by man since the first land surface was elevated above the sea. Geological erosion, over long ages of time, wears down mountains and fills up depressions. But it progresses slowly. Nature clothes her humid hills with trees and her subhumid swells of land with grass. This vegetation is a protective canopy over the soil, furnishing protection from the pounding and at the same time loosening effect of the rain. The accumulated litter of leaves and stems soaks up the water and lets it seep away into soil made porous by the organic accumulation in and on the surface. A binding net-

2 A. F. Gustafson, *The Control of Soil Erosion in New York* (Cornell Extension Bulletin 438, 1940), 8.

work of roots holds the soil against water that does run off. The slow process of erosion in a balanced natural environment is generally no more rapid than the formation of new soil from the parent soil materials beneath. It is a normal process, seldom harmful and often beneficial. Over the ages it has moved much fertile soil material downhill on to plains and into valleys where the maximum agricultural value may be realized. The alluvial flood plains of streams (generally speaking, the most fertile soils of the world) have accumulated in this manner.

It is "accelerated" erosion, brought about by the removal of nature's protective cover from the land, that is destructive of soil and against which a farmer must guard if his soil is to be kept at maximum productivity. The numberless tiny dams formed by the vegetative debris and the binding roots, each minor in itself but great in the aggregate, are lost. Gravity, unchecked, may then result in excessive and destructive runoff from land that tilts up on edge. The loss of the moisture that runs away may in itself be a limiting factor in crop growth on sloping fields, and the loss of soil particles and plant nutrients carried away with it may be still further limiting.

But with a dense crop growth performing the same function as the original land cover, the farmer may check erosion to the point of almost completely stopping it on fields that, left bare, would be seriously damaged. Results of erosion experiments by the Soil Conservation Service bear this out.

Annual Soil and Water Losses per Acre at Erosion Experiment Stations of the Soil Conservation Service[3]

Location	Annual precipi- tation	Slope of land	Clean-tilled crop		Dense cover- thick-growing crop		Number of years to remove 7 inches of topsoil	
			Ann'l soil loss	Ann'l water loss	Ann'l soil loss	Ann'l water loss	Clean tillage	Dense cover
	INCHES	%	TONS	%*	TONS	%*	NO.	NO.
Bethany, Mo.	35	8.0	69	28	0.3	9	16	3,900
Tyler, Tex.	41	8.8	28	21	0.1	1	49	11,100
Guthrie, Okla.	33	7.7	24	14	0.03	1	50	38,200
Clarinda, Ia.	27	9.0	19	7	0.06	1	48	15,200
Statesville, N. C.	45	10.0	23	10	0.01	0.3	51	95,800

* Per cent of total precipitation

[3] Bennett and Lowdermilk, "General Aspects of the Erosion Problem," *Soils and Men*, 594.

When dense cover, such as is provided by thick-growing grass and legumes, is kept upon the land, losses of both soil and water are practically eliminated. Erosion has been stopped; rainfall is held upon the land until it soaks in. The length of time required for seven inches of topsoil to erode away (as estimated from the rates of erosion reported from the Soil Conservation Service's experiments) is lengthened to many hundreds of years, even on 8 to 10 per cent slopes. Similar fields devoted continuously to cultivated row crops have been known to lose their topsoil within the farming lifetimes of a father-and-son succession on the land.

Mention has already been made of the tendency of soils (particularly heavy soils) to harden after they have been cropped for some time and the humus content has been depleted. The porous, friable structure of the soil is reduced. Susceptibility to erosion is increased because the soil can soak up less water—more is left to run off. Crops grow less well in the hardened, depleted soil, thus providing a less dense cover that further increases possible erosion damage. Obviously, the maintenance of fertility and the problem of erosion are inseparably tied together.

Charles E. Kellogg, chief of the Soil Survey, says: "A great deal of erosion has commenced after the land was farmed for some time; it followed a decrease in organic matter, plant nutrients, and productivity. Of course, the erosion itself will decrease productivity even further by removing the friable surface soil and exposing a lower layer of poorer structure, and by reducing organic matter and plant nutrients, especially nitrogen and available phosphorous, since these are frequently more abundant in the surface horizons than in the lower horizons. Thus accelerated erosion is a symptom of declining productivity, but this initial cause may be intensified by the erosion itself. A sort of vicious circle develops."[4]

No farmer, who is himself the victim of erosion to the degree where the ribs of the subsoil show through the surface, needs to be told that crop yields are greatly reduced on such fields. Compared to the topsoil, the subsoil usually contains less nutrients, is harder, and will retain less moisture—all of which are conditions detrimental to crop growth. Any farmer who still has his topsoil, but who might not continue to have it if erosion is not guarded against,

[4] *The Soils That Support Us* (copyright 1941 by The Macmillan Company, New York), 246–47.

should take heed from other experiments conducted by the Soil Conservation Service.

Yields of Seed Cotton from Fertilized and Unfertilized Plots of Normal and Desurfaced Soils[5]

Location	Average yield per acre, normal soil		Average yield per acre, desurfaced soil	
	Unfertilized	Fertilized*	Unfertilized	Fertilized*
	POUNDS	POUNDS	POUNDS	POUNDS
Tyler, Tex.	360	380	50	225
Statesville, N. C.	934	——	225	727

* Fertilizer treatment: Tyler, Texas; normal soil, 400 pounds 4–12–4 per acre; desurfaced soil, 400 pounds of 4–12–4 per acre and oats plowed under as green manure. Statesville, N. C.: normal soil not fertilized; desurfaced soil, 600 pounds of 5–10–3 per acre and cowpeas plowed under as green manure.

The desurfaced soils used in these tests were purposely stripped of the topsoil for the purpose of the experiment. The results reported are the average yields for four years. Even with green manure and fairly liberal applications of chemical fertilizer each year, the desurfaced soils at Tyler yielded only 61 per cent as much cotton as normal soil without either fertilizer or green manure; at Statesville, only 77 per cent as much.

Some farmers have more of an erosion problem than others. Steps to be taken for control are dictated by individual circumstances. The rate of water erosion varies with slope, with the porosity and perviousness of the soil, with the seasonality and intensity of rainfall, with the length of time the soil is frozen each year, with the length of time and season of the year during which the soil is bare of cover, and with the kind of crops grown. These variables are so great and of so many possible combinations that the proper control measures on one farm or one field may be entirely unsuitable in another location.

Yet some principles may be established.

The most effective control of water and soil losses on sloping land is a dense sod of perennial grasses and legumes. It is one of nature's controls, and the farmer can improve upon it only by stimulating heavier and more dense growth than would develop

5 Utz, Kellogg, Reed, Stallings, and Munns in *Soils and Men*, 103.

under natural conditions alone. The steeper the slope, or more erodible the soil, or the heavier the rainfall, the more necessary this type of control becomes.

Many thousands of acres of land, too steep and too crosive to be continued successfully in clean cultivation (or even in rotations including cultivated crops), may still be used and maintained if seeded down to perennial grasses and legumes and kept in those crops. The necessity for this adjustment has long been obvious. But some farmers have been reticent to make it because the income from an acre of pasture or hay is less than from an acre of cultivated crop if a good yield can be obtained from the latter.

More and more it is becoming apparent, however, that fairly productive pasture or meadow is more profitable than crop failure resulting from continued erosion.

One of the greatest drawbacks to achieving a truly national program of conservation is the farmers' stalwart adhesion to a traditional farming pattern. No matter how logical the argument or how dramatic the demonstration, and even if a conversion to the new way is gained, some farmers insist on going back to the old pattern after trying the conservation method.

In Oklahoma, Harley A. Daniel and his colleagues of the Guthrie Conservation Station succeeded in getting much nearly sterile cotton acreage changed into pasture land. The fields so changed had been reduced to yields of only one hundred pounds of lint per acre. At prewar prices this meant that the land was not returning seed and fertilizer costs.

A program of brush and rock dams in the gullies was instituted. Grass was seeded back in some places; in others, fertilization brought in natural grasses. This worthless land then was pastured to beef cattle and showed a return of twenty-five to fifty pounds of beef per acre during summer grazing. Certainly this return did not compare with what the land had given when it still had its topsoil and cotton prices were good, but the capital value of once worthless land was being enhanced each year and the return that did come in had a very high net.

But, to the grave disappointment of the conservation workers, when the land was green again and cotton prices rose, the owners in some cases went right back to planting cotton. What was worse —despite the object lesson given, despite the previous frightful losses—the cotton planters ran the rows up and down the hills just as they had always done. Where terracing had been instituted, they plowed across the earth structures; and the rains washed down the rows just as they had before. Once again the soil headed for infertility and inevitable abandonment.

Seeding cropland down to grass may force other changes in farm organization. Only forage-consuming livestock can use the grass advantageously. Less cash cropping and more cattle is a change that must and will take place in American agriculture if erosion losses are to be reduced. Postwar surpluses may speed the coming of a widespread pasture economy, particularly in parts of the South and the East. Many present farms are too small to make economic-sized "grass and cattle" units. Thus another adjustment, fewer and larger farms, will be necessary in many areas—particularly of the South and the East.

Not all sloping land, by any means, must be seeded to grass. By planting row crops across the slope of a field rather than up and down the slope, some land that would otherwise be disastrously eroded may be used for cultivated crops. Each row, with the minor ridges developed in planting and cultivation, then becomes a tiny check dam that will impound some water until it soaks away. Up-and-down rows, by contrast, merely invite runoff and erosion by concentrating water into the cultivation furrows.

Wide interest has recently developed in strip cropping, a system of erosion control in which each crop in the rotation is grown in strips that run along the slope—a strip of corn, a strip of hay, a strip of oats, and so on, with each strip being rotated to each crop in its proper turn. The strips may be wide or narrow depending upon the erodibility of the soil. All rows follow the contour of the land. Whatever runoff does occur from the cultivated strips is caught and held by sod strips below. It is a system admirably suited to many sloping fields; but, of course, like any other one method of control, it is not a universal erosion cure-all.

An objection that some farmers have had to strip cropping is that it would create, they felt, many small patches of each crop, complicating the work of growing and harvesting. But others, who, by removing fence rows and other obstructions to tillage, have been able to lay out strips that were long even though narrow, have found this difficulty to be minor.

Interesting results have been obtained in a study in Illinois where production on fields where crops were planted in strips along the contour of the slope has been compared over the six-year period 1939–44 with production on the same farms on similarly sloping fields that were not contoured.

Yields of Crops on Contoured Fields and Non-contoured
Fields on the Same Farms in Illinois, 1939–1944[6]

	Corn	Soybeans	Oats	Wheat
		Yield per acre, bushels		
Contoured fields	66	23	44	22
Non-contoured fields	59	20	37	19

"The increased production from conservation practices or 'around-the-hill' farming was equivalent to having 12 per cent more land in corn, 13 per cent more in soybeans, and 18 per cent more in oats and wheat.

"In addition to conserving soil and moisture and increasing yields, contour farming saves fuel and reduces wear and tear on machinery. Results of a study on which all or the major part of the farming operations were on the contour, matched with neighboring farms on which no field operations were on the contour, indicate that for the four years, 1940–43, power and machinery costs were 36 cents per crop acre less and labor costs 84 cents less on the contour-operated farms.

"While contour farming and other conservation practices to fit the farming pattern to the natural lay of the land so as to get the crop rows on the level is relatively new in most of Illinois, it was recognized as desirable by some of our earliest leaders. Thomas Jefferson wrote in 1813 regarding his farm: 'We now plow horizontally, following the curvatures of the hills and hollows, on the dead level, however crooked the lines may be. Every furrow thus acts as a reservoir to receive and retain the waters, all of which go to the benefit of the growing plant, instead of running off into the streams. The horses draw much easier on the dead level and it is in fact a conversion of hilly grounds into a plain.' The usual up-and-down hill farming hastens erosion and soil depletion and in-

6 E. L. Sauer, "It's Profitable to Farm on the Level, *Illinois Farm Economics*, March, 1945, 207.

tensifies the 'downs' of the ups and downs of farm income. Farmers who have had experience with conservation practices take as much pride in their level curving rows and fields as they formerly did in their straight up-and-down hill rows and fields."[7]

Grass on some slopes, strip cropping on others, low terraces and diversion ditches where needed, wind breaks, wind-stripping, and stubble mulching—each is an erosion-control practice. No one is a panacea. Each has its place in contributing to soil maintenance and, therefore, to successful soil management. A few fortunately located farmers may have no erosion problem. Others may protect their land by some single, simple practice such as contour farming. For still others on the more erodible land, no one preventive measure will suffice; they must literally throw in the book (even to the extreme of changing their type of farming) if their land is to be preserved and maintained. Conditions on each individual farm determine the steps that must be taken, and the farmer who will be successful must face the matter squarely.

On a national basis, soil erosion, like other forms of soil depletion, is a major problem. But for the individual farmer, it is his problem. Continued, unchecked erosion piles up grief not only for succeeding generations, but also for the farmer now on the land.

6. Inventory before Planning

THE number of soil types in the United States that have been distinguished and individually named is so great that a large book would be required simply to list them. They vary from one another in every imaginable way—in origin, in development, in depth, in drainage, in structure, in texture, in acidity (or alkalinity), in plant-nutrient content, in nutrient availability, and in response to management. Some must be handled very delicately, are productive if they are and useless if they are not. Others may even be abused for considerable time (though not indefinitely) and still suffer little loss in fertility. Some are naturally highly fertile, and their fertility may easily and inexpensively be maintained. Others are naturally infertile but are highly responsive to intelligent man-

[7] Sauer, "It's Profitable to Farm on the Level," *Illinois Farm Economics*, March, 1945, 206–207.

agement. Still others are infertile, and for no expenditure that can be justified economically can they be made fertile.

Some soils were settled and farmed for one or more generations, only to be abandoned because they produced so little that the families on them could not make a living. Many of the so-called "worn-out" soils, particularly in the East, were never at any time much more productive than when they were abandoned. Some were abandoned, the records show us, almost immediately after settlement. Still other soils that are now derelict supported farm families reasonably well in the days of more self-sufficient agriculture but cannot meet the competition in the high-yield, low-cost commercial farming of today.

Yes, and there are other lands on which owners have looked for a last time, locked the gate (or not bothered to), and left, not to return—the reason for their going being simply depletion, erosion, and neglect of soil that had once been fertile. Young and adolescent America has seen much of this. It looks foolish to us now in a more mature age, and it will be considered, rightly, as criminal when the country reaches its majority.

Some derelict lands may be brought back into usefulness; others are not worth the cost in relation to their potential productivity and the country's peacetime need for their produce. The cry is recurrent to bring all abandoned farmlands back into production and on the tax rolls. The desirability of doing so at any time must be determined in terms of cost and value, with an answer individually determined for each separate parcel of land. The concept of maximum social benefit would indicate that any land area or land parcel that requires more public service and expense than its potential production will support is a doubtful asset in the society within which it is included. Different values and different measures of contribution will obviously prevail at different times. But at least this concept should apply to the rehabilitation programs for derelict farmland.

All land has a possible economic use—some for cropping, some for pasture, some for forests, some for recreation and scenery; some land is, in fact, mere economic void, useful only to hold more productive places apart. Any difference in point of view between those who would define differently the land that should be farmed is merely one of degree—one of where they would draw the lines.

44

Whatever the public policy or point of view should be, the farm-management point of view is concrete and concise—it is that of the individual business operation. Soil is an essential factor of production in farming. How well one manages it is the most potent determinant of his continuing success.

Land may be skinned and depleted, either purposely or through ignorance. But farming is a conservative, long-time business, producing at the maximum only modest profits even when soil fertility is sold off quickly. In a lifetime of farming one can obtain a much greater total return from his soil by retaining a high state of productivity for the beginning of each new crop-year —and you want a good living for a lifetime, not just for a few years. "Management for immediate gain is thus contrasted to management for secure production."[1]

There is a useful concept in forestry that may be carried over into soil management; it is production on a sustained-yield basis. In forestry it means cutting only in proportion to growth so that the resource is not depleted. In soil management it means a conservation of fertility in contrast to depletion. Here is the essential difference between production from the soil and the extraction of minerals. Soils can be used and maintained indefinitely; mines cannot.

Soil conservation does not mean simply saving, or denial, of use. Rather, as Kellogg says, it implies use—full use—on a sustained-yield basis for secure, continuing production. And how well any soil produces, and continues to produce comes back to management. Some farmers are more successful with mediocre soils than are others with the best. They are the ones who know their soils, their peculiarities and responses. Farmers such as these manage well.

Soil is a natural body of the utmost complexity in its nature and behavior. Thousands of practical farmers and hundreds of patient scientists have devoted much of their lives to tracking down some of its secrets. Hundreds of books have been published to present their findings. This short discussion of the complex question of soil management must of necessity be superficial. We make no claim for its exhaustiveness. Many of the statements are over-

1 Kellogg, *The Soils That Support Us,* 259.

simplifications. Our intention is solely to establish the importance of intelligent soil management in the still bigger job of successful farm-business management, and to support our position.

Our belief is this: Any farmer who would be a successful husbandman should be willing and aggressive in the study of his own soil—the basis for his business. He should make a soil inventory of his property, correctly describing each field—its status, its needs, and the manner of fulfilling those needs. First, he should find out what his soil types are and their characteristics. Will they best respond to deep or shallow tillage? Have they been much or little leached? Do they normally tend toward the acid, or is there sufficient available calcium in the underlay to require little surface application of lime? Is the organic content at an optimum level?

What crops are best suited to the soil types available? What about the physical layout of the fields from a working and erosion standpoint? Should the field patterns as found be left in existence or would a rearrangement of the farm be of value soil-wise? (For instance, it might be economical and make for better farming if fence rows were changed to put all of one soil type in one field and another in a second rather than to try and manage both types in a single field.)

Such data will be a major help in mapping out an economical and efficient rotation. Whether or not the rotation will produce adequate income considering the farm site in relation to markets is a question to settle before purchase. Possibly the best crop practice and the only one which will preserve capital investment may be one that would not provide a living on the farm at its present size. Obviously, then, more land must be purchased, or the whole project given up. In only too many cases, the latter decision is the better.

The past history of the production of a farm is sometimes of little value when an appraisal is made. Maybe the production records were at the expense of soil fertility. Maybe markets have changed, and the only crops feasible on the soil types are not now profitable. The time to find out these facts is before a farm enterprise is set up.

Suppose, however, that a farmer is already on the land. He is worried about his inability to make a good living. He decides to make a thorough analysis of his position to see if he can find

In 1876, when this sloping Dallas County, Texas, land was first put
under cultivation, the fields on both sides of the fence were probably the same elevation. Cotton and corn ruined the right-hand
field. Native Bluestem cover saved the left-hand field.

Where slope and soil type constitute an erosion threat, even orchards should be planted on the contour, as in the case of this Berrien County, Michigan, peach orchard.

some way out of his dilemma. After a soil survey and evaluation he finds that it is unlikely he will ever be able to make a success on the size farm he has. Maybe the best thing he can do in that case is to seed his entire place to grass, rent it out as pasture, and go to work for wages to get more capital to expand his operation into a feasible economic unit. Or, maybe, he should sell some of the land and turn to poultry or some other endeavor which does away with row cropping. If these suggestions are not acceptable, perhaps his best plan would be to go to a neighbor similarly situated, show that neighbor that he is faced with the same dilemma, then sell out to him if the latter can afford to buy. With the money thus acquired, the first man could turn elsewhere to a better proposition.

The one lesson management should teach is the proper evaluation of a property. If that property does not have a chance over the ten-year average to yield a good living, the management-wise farmer should have the courage to turn away from it. He is more than foolish to do as so many do—stubbornly stick on the land in the hope that a "good year," or government largesse, will make up for what is an economically unsound deal to start with. The reason that one-third of all the farms make only 10 per cent of the national farm income is that under modern conditions many of them cannot be successfully farmed in the traditional pattern of the past. Good managers cannot afford to let tradition stand in the way of recognition of truth.

If a farm has no chance because of soil type and size to make a decent annual wage but if the social and aesthetic values of country living appeal highly to the owner, then another thoroughly modern plan is worth consideration. It is to put the farm on a part-time basis and secure cash income from an outside or off-the-farm activity. Thus, a dairy farm in the Northeast too small or with too much rough pasturage and woods to support a herd large enough to return a living, might be changed into a home with garden attached and only sufficient livestock to provide for family needs. The children of the family might be all the labor force required on such a place. The father could work for other farmers—probably using the machinery he has and purchasing more to become a custom operator. He could be a mechanic, a mason, a carpenter, or other skilled worker. Or he could commute to a near-by town or village, finding work in trade, transportation, or construction.

The possibilities are many, but vary with the location. For a man who knows only farming they may seem limited unless he is willing to learn new tricks. But, unless he is resigned to fighting a losing game, unless he does not mind having his children reared in a rural slum, some hundreds of thousands of him would be better off today finding another line of work rather than hopelessly trying to make a go of an impossible venture. Endless subsidies and permanent erection of a false price structure for farm products will not solve his problems. They treat only the effect and leave the cause untouched.

Against these cases are, however, many enterprises which now are doing poorly but could be turned into successes by proper management practices. If the soil types will support a commercial project, given proper size and management, it is perfectly possible that a shrewd manager can succeed where others have failed. Aiding this type of man is one of the main purposes of this book.

A good manager will never stop studying his soils. He will watch their response to tillage and to fertilization. He will find out by actual trial whether fall or spring plowing is best for him. He will frequently test the moisture-holding capacity of the upper layers of soil, while he is ever on the alert to prevent erosion by water or wind, remembering that sheet erosion is as costly as gullying if not so dramatic in appearance.

There is no substitute for first-hand personal acquaintance with one's soil. The reason many ethnic groups from older countries failed on American soils is that they thought the land on which they settled was the same as that whence they had come, because of a superficial resemblance of the color or texture of the soil. Experience proved the error, but few stayed long enough to find out how to manage the new soils. In other regions such as Lancaster, Pennsylvania, the newcomers thought they were on soils similar to those they had left behind—and they were right. Their success is one of the bright spots in American agriculture.

Under old methods and the little knowledge of the composition and chemistry of soils available, the only recourse yesterday's husbandman had was to spend a generation of trial and error to find out the best way to handle his land. Then, unless he had passed his knowledge on to somebody else, the next operator had to start all over again.

Today, however, the good manager can speed the acquiring of knowledge of his soil and can obtain a good working relationship in a much shorter time than used to be possible. The sooner he does this, the quicker his start on the road to success. Every farmer should remember these things: Work with your soil, not against it. Help Nature build a deep, mellow, humus-laden layer that will be the best heritage you can pass on to your heirs.

PART II: Equipment Management

"Tools can keep you in the black,
or dump you in the red."

7. From Crooked Stick to Electric Eye

FOR thousands of years farm equipment remained essentially unchanged—and it still is in many countries, including parts of our own United States. One of the most startling facts about equipment is its comparative youth, for it is scarcely a century old, though farming is the most venerable of human endeavors.

A Scot invented a threshing machine about the time of the American Revolution, but little more than the fact of the inventing was ever heard of it. A short time later, Thomas Jefferson carved out a wooden model of the plow as we know it today. Most historians date the beginning of farm machinery with the famed farmer of Shadwell, although others start only a hundred years ago with Cyrus McCormick and the reaper. The time of the beginning of the farm-equipment industry makes little difference to the modern farm manager other than to imply that an industry so new must have a great deal more to contribute in the years just ahead.

By the eighties, the steam tractor made its appearance. It was an unwieldy Rube Goldberg–looking contraption. It had a very bad habit of burning the crops in the fields it was working. Few people thought it was here to stay; yet during World War II old steamers (which have not been manufactured since 1910) were hauled out, refurbished, and made a definite contribution to American production.

The turn of the century saw steam power made obsolete by the internal-combustion engine. World War I proved this motive power valuable and permanent, but the majority of farmers thought it would never supplant the horse. It was believed to be useful chiefly on large western grain ranches. However, in the early nineteen twenties the row-crop tractor made its appearance, and shortly thereafter its use began to spread to all parts of the country and into all crops.

In the meantime, most of the basic tools we know today had been invented and their forms fairly well set. Thus the mower changed little in a half-century. Disks, harrows, plows, binders, even the hay loader were essentially the same design that our grandfathers had used. Tractor tools, as such, lagged behind the introduction of mechanical power. Usually a farmer bought a tractor, then either bought or constructed a hitch which would enable him to utilize his horse-drawn equipment. The results were not always too happy and frequently were no improvement over the old ways. As a consequence, a number of tractors were used only sparingly, many were merely adjuncts to basic animal power, and some were turned back to the sellers because the farmers using them branded them definite failures.

In the early nineteen thirties farm power machinery at last came of age; that is, until then the whole idea had been to get a substitute for the horse, with little thought of having it do more than the horse could do. The arguments for mechanical power were that the machine did not tire, did not sweat, and did not have to be rested at the end of the row. Much was made of the fact that power machines not in use cost nothing to feed and required no care, thus making the cost of housing a machine and its "feed" a fraction of that of housing animals and their feed. Until the sights of agriculturists were raised from merely substituting for the horse to the new conception of power farming as a wholly different operation with vastly wider horizons, farm machinery was still piddling along in the old ways, looking for minute improvements rather than a whole new technique.

The coming of rubber to the farm was the circumstance that did more to change farming practice than any other factor in thousands of years.

That broad statement is put in purposely to shock. The basis for it is that farming until that time had been geared to the walk of a man. True, riding cultivators and plows were known, but farming as a whole was still mentally geared at walking speed. Rubberizing machines meant taking the ceiling off speed. However, almost at once, the farmer found the rate not unlimited. Tools designed for horses performed their jobs poorly when speed-

51

ed up. Hence tools specifically designed for tractor power made their appearance.

We still have not found out how to do a proper job of mold-board plowing much faster than when the horse pulled the plow, although we have made multiple bottoms more common. We have found other means of seedbed preparation that definitely are faster than the traditional, such as the multi-gang one-way plow. A horse mower with a tractor hitch did not speed mowing greatly, but a power take-off mower on rubber did. Many of the tractor tools which are essentially still horse-drawn designs do not show any great speed-up, but now that designers think in terms of greater mileage per hour, there is an obvious tendency to increase speed, size, and scope. Most important of all, the newer designers are getting away from the traditional thought that machinery must necessarily be pulled. The tractor develops its best efforts as a pusher. That fact means a whole new concept of power application. At this writing, we may confidently say that we are only now (after World War II) on the threshold of power farming.

In the years just ahead, farming will undoubtedly catch up with industry in machinery adaptation, flow-line techniques, and even mass production in some crops such as cotton. Farming is at a point in its mechanical revolution comparable to the position of manufacturing at the turn of the century. However, it should take agriculture much less than half a century to get on a par with industrial manufacturing in applying the contributions from pure and applied research.

What the resulting change will mean in economic and sociological values is not easy to foretell. Certainly, it will not all be good for all farmers. For instance, greater mechanization means greater capitalization per farm. That, in turn, means more stratification between various farm levels. Oddly enough, further mechanization puts a greater premium than ever on soil types and conditions. It is true that mechanization of the corn crop was one of the really big helps to wartime production. Without the new machines, we should have had shortages that not only would have been more serious but might have been disastrous. Nevertheless, even though machines do help in many respects to overcome unfortunate climatic and soil conditions and sometimes are of vast aid, because of economics and the limitations of mechanization, some soil types and conditions will be little touched and some actually hindered. Hence, one farmer will speed ahead while another will be hobbled competitively by the difference in soils.

In the past, tools have been bought for almost every reason except that resulting from hard figuring of first cost, operating cost, depreciation, and effective hours of work per year. Tools have been bought because they were vaguely "labor saving." The mere fact of saving labor may be a sociological good in itself, but it is not necessarily profitable, economical, nor conducive to the greatest long-term good. Rating of equipment should always start with costs in terms of investment in dollars and of best utilization of labor. It is quite possible that on one farm a certain tool rated by these criteria would prove to cost the operator more than any possible money saving. Still, he might want that tool regardless of economy.

For instance, a small dairy farmer in the Northeast might have the capital to buy a $500 barn-gutter cleaner that would save him four hundred hours of labor a year. But if he has little field work, buys most of his feed, and his labor input averages less than a moderate working day, he would be buying a luxury that he could by no means justify, even though he could afford it. If he wants it anyway, justified or not, it is certainly his privilege to acquire it, even though the act could not be rated as "good management." However, if he took those four hundred hours and put them into profit-making work, such as handling more animals, then the situation would change materially. Therefore, good equipment management must always take into consideration not only labor saving but also labor utilization. Energy saved does not create wealth. Producing more goods can.

8. The Five Classes of Tools

TILLAGE IMPLEMENTS

TO suggest that the selection of tillage tools requires serious consideration may seem unnecessary attention to detail. However, the farmer does not haphazardly purchase a plow, a disk, and a harrow. If that were all there is to selection, why should one

53

manufacturer alone list over one hundred models? Certainly it is not to "get rich quick," for he could much more profitably manufacture one hundred machines of a single type than he does his present many and varied models. In fact, if he could cut his display to even ten or fifteen types, he could reduce prices, give better service, and probably increase his sales. Without doubt he would make a bigger profit, while his dealers would rise up and call him their greatest friend. Nevertheless, the fact remains that farmers have demanded and have had designed a different kind of plow for almost every recognized soil and topographic condition.

What is the right plow for a particular farm? If that question could be answered quickly and easily, and the proper plow sold to each farmer, manufacturers would indeed be pleased. Probably no other tool in agriculture arouses more argument than the plow with its infinite variations—there are even the Faulkners who would do away with it entirely. This should be a good place to start the inquiry, for not all farms need a plow—some farms, indeed, should not have one, and some should have a tool of special design.

First of all, are you farming on a heavy soil, in a humid region, and do you wish to bury all trash cleanly? If so, most agronomists would agree that you need a moldboard plow. But if you are on a light soil, in the blowing region of the Western Plains, more than likely you need a "one-way." If you are in a prospective Dust Bowl area, you may want to by-pass even the "one-way" and establish a system of trash- or stubble-mulch farming, in which case you will need new tools, some of which scarcely have commercial names as yet. They are designed not to turn under all surface plants and residues but to put only a portion of the trash below the surface and leave the remainder on top though firmly anchored.

Mack Gowder, the farmer near Atlanta, Georgia, mentioned in Chapter 2, may go down in agricultural history as one of the great pioneers in new tillage practices. For over two decades he has farmed a Georgia hill farm without plowing. He uses what he calls a "bull-tongue scooter." While his neighbors' lands have run down the hillsides until little fertile soil is left, his soil has built in depth and richness with resulting ever greater yields, and at the same time he has increased his capital assets.

There are listers, middle-busters, basin listers, prairie-plows, reversible plows, and rotary-tillage tools—to name just a few of the possibilities. Each of them has its place. Your task is to find out what is best for your farm.

Because it cannot be emphasized too much, your first consideration should be: What is the best conservation practice for me? Start by holding your capital, not by seeking immediate profits. Choose the basic tillage tool which will do most to hold your soil. Who should advise you? Why not the Soil Conservation Service representative in your district? He should know your type of soil from his soil maps. He should know what your drainage, erosion, and conservation problems are. If he does not, he will be glad to examine your place and find out. While he is there, ask him to recommend field layout, strip cropping, terracing, or whatever other conservation practices should be employed.

When you know what should be done to conserve fertility, the soil itself, and your water supply, you should stop to take stock of your farm plans and your finances. Possibly you may then argue that you cannot afford to make conservation your major interest. Maybe you will say that you must get crops coming quickly to turn into dollars to pay on the mortgage. If that is your situation, you are entering a business too far underfinanced to hope for ultimate success. The day of mining the soil, of taking quick returns, and then moving on to the next location is over. It never was the best practice. Now it is definitely against the public good. It is not at all far fetched to look to the time, in the not too distant future, when as a matter of public policy a man's individual dictatorship over his own soil will not be permitted. America's soil is not in the sole possession of whoever owns the deed. America's soil, on your farm or your neighbor's, is part of the heritage of every citizen. When you or anyone else wastes that fertility for an immediate dollar, part of the national capital has been expended for personal gain. Not only is that unpatriotic; it is unfair to all of tomorrow's citizens, be they farmers or city men.

Under a proper soil-conservation program, your soil can be saved and can be improved. Moreover, it will produce greater personal returns for you in the long run, besides leaving behind a better farm for your children and better opportunities for them than you had. Again, it must be emphasized if you must get this season's crop at the expense of your capital, you are underfinanced. You should not be farming at all unless and until you can afford to protect your own, and the nation's, investment. Better work a year or so longer at your job, better lease or share crop, until you have the finances to treat your farm as a permanent industry, one that will give you greater yields ten years from now.

Accordingly, the first thing to decide is not which of a hundred plow designs you want, but whether you want to plow or not, and, if you do, how. Keep in mind that while the plow has been called the greatest of all friends to man, it has also been declared to be mankind's greatest enemy, even long before Faulkner—the agricultural history of Palestine certainly gives ample evidence of the validity of the statement. The first principle, then, in your selection of basic tillage tools is not seed- or root-bed preparation, as has frequently been taught, but what tools should be used and what tools and practices avoided to conserve capital investment.

The choice of the other fitting tools will depend upon your crop plan, your soil, and the pitch of your land. In some soils and for some crops you will find a rotary hoe, a roller, or a cutout disk desirable. Your county agent should know. Or you may write your state extension agronomist, giving soil type, crops to be planted, and all other pertinent data so that he can return an accurate recommendation. Proper seedbed fitting is a different problem in every part of the country. It may be different on your farm from that on your neighbor's land just over the fence. Also, there is at least a chance that your neighbor is not doing the best possible job of preparing his own seedbeds. Therefore, do not depend on local custom nor what you may have learned someplace else. Instead, for best results get a tailored plan for your own farm. Then become a research man yourself and experiment to find ways of improving your own practices, for this facet of agronomy still is far from completely explored. A tremendous amount of work has been done; a tremendous amount remains to be done. Some of the most interesting possibilities are being suggested by experimentally minded farmers as well as by professional agronomists.

For example, one farmer found that by cross-plowing, then cross-disking, he obtained significant increases in yields. His neighbor followed the same practices, but when he figured his costs, the increase in yield was not justified by the additional expense of seedbed fitting. The difference in soil type could easily be an explanation of this situation.

How many plow bottoms should you operate? That depends not only on operating costs but also on soil and climate. One of the authors took over the management of a farm in an area where all farmers used two-bottom plows no matter what the size of the project, the number of acres to be plowed each year, or the actual experience in the plowing operation. Two-bottom plows were the rule, and everyone slavishly followed that rule. At one time the farms, on the average, had been larger. They had been horse-farmed, of course, and much acreage had been given over to grain and forage production when the two-bottom plow had first come to favor.

In later years the type of farming changed. Units became smaller. Horses disappeared. Concentrates were bought, generally, rather than raised. Most plowing was for rotation pastures, while row or grain crops were dropped almost completely except for some ensilage corn. Watching neighbors plow trashy and run-out pastures, the observer was struck by the amount of time the operator wasted in getting off the tractor to clean the fouled-up bottoms. Another notable observation was the time and fuel waste in swinging the two-bottoms around in the crowded headlands. The conclusion was reached that, as most of the fields were small and as fouling of the two-bottoms seemed to cause much loss of time, perhaps a single-bottom plow would in the long run be a more efficient tool.

The equipment distributor tried sincerely to dissuade the newcomer from any such heresy. He pointed out all the well-to-do natives who had made their money with two-bottom plows. Nevertheless, the order for a single-bottom plow remained. Even upon delivery the distressed dealer mentioned that he knew a "sucker" who would take the offending implement off the buyer's hands.

Some years have passed. Many farmers in the community still have two-bottom plows. But about sixty have changed to the single-bottom. And the dealer now has the original single-bottom, bought by the newcomer, at work on his own place. After watching the self-cleaning ability of the single-bottom and reckoning the acreage plowed in a day by the supposedly "expensive" tool, the dealer borrowed it for his own work. Later, he had used it so much and had sold so many more that he felt he should replace the fairly worn tool by giving a new one to the original buyer.

The object of this story is not that everyone in heavy, trashy soils should select a single-bottom plow. It is to illustrate another principle of tool selection: Observation and common horse sense are two of the greatest assets of the good manager. Yesterday's methods are not necessarily the best. General recommendations by the highest authorities may not fit your community. Not only are research, trying out a new idea, or even on occasion retrying an old one (for farm patterns are changing all the while) desirable practices; they are mandatory to keep ahead of the game.

CROP-STARTING TOOLS

Ever since all-out mechanization came to American farms, there has been a growing wail that some tools cost too much for the amount of use they get. The manufacturer says that he is help-less to reduce prices as long as volume remains low. Hence the farmer is faced with what seems to be an overinvestment; or he buys secondhand to try to keep investment down; or he tries rent-ing, borrowing, custom work, or co-operative or group ownership.

From a standpoint of getting the work done at precisely the best time, there may be no adequate substitute for ownership. Dependence on others may throw off the entire field schedule. Weather may permit only a now-and-then entrance to the fields; and thus the farmer needs planting and fertilizing equipment on hand and ready to go all through the seeding season.

During the war years we had ample illustration of the benefits of mechanization. Under old methods and without modern ma-chinery, it is reasonably certain that our national corn crop would have fallen far below minimum needs. But because of mechanized power and new and more efficient tools moving at good speeds for long hours, it was possible to get the crops in, even though floods, droughts, and unseasonable weather of every kind afflicted the Corn Belt at one planting time or another. This experience sug-gests that here is another phase of farm management where there is no satisfactory substitute for sufficient capital.

Another practice that indicates sole ownership is the increased use of fertilizer. Before World War II, only the South, the North-east, and some specialized crop regions such as Tidewater, Vir-ginia, were heavy and consistent users of fertilizers. Now we know that almost all humid-region lands that have been farmed for long need, and can use economically, annual applications of lime and fertilizer. Also, we know that lime, for instance, can be applied at almost any time during the year. Fertilizer may be successfully used at various seasons, not just at planting as was previously believed. This means that work can be spread more evenly and that time can be utilized more efficiently. It also means that more annual use of the tools is possible and desirable.

Here let us call attention to the new combination machines, such as the fertilizer attachment for plows that puts the fertilizer on the plow sole or mixes it with the turning furrow. There is a definite trend toward combining fertilizing with other operations at a saving in time and in capital investment in machines.

In the category of crop-starting tools, there is one which can be the most useful machine on the farm—if it is used as much as it ought to be. That one is the manure spreader. In many areas manure has been spread only at the long convenience of the farmer —when there was nothing else to do, or when the manure pile got out of hand. Now we know that the longer manure stays in the pile the greater the losses of plant nutrients. On many a well-managed livestock farm, manure is spread every day in the year that it is possible to get on the fields. On others, manure is delivered from barn directly to covered pit, treated with superphosphate, then applied when field conditions are right. In humid regions, losses on the field through leaching are liable to be great if too long a time elapses between application and turning under.

In the past, manure spreaders have been one of the most damned tools on the farm. They seemed to be forever breaking. Their construction was looked upon as unnecessarily fragile, and many a manufacturer has been roundly criticized. The putting of the machines on rubber did much to curb the criticism and bring relief to the operators. Now it is possible to get two-wheeled spreaders that hitch directly to the tractor. Spreaders are appearing with power take-off drive instead of ground wheel, and spreaders with their own auxiliary motors are here, while an experimental model on runners, made and forgotten many years ago, is again trying for a comeback, for in the colder regions there is a place for such a machine.

The best management practice so far as crop-starting tools are concerned is to own your own, then conserve them. Planters do not have to last just a short time. They do not have to break at just the crucial moment. Today there are rust-proof compounds that will extend their life. There never was a good reason why these tools should not be entirely overhauled and worn parts replaced during the winter months. A little oil here; some equipment-paint there; rust-proofing on wearing surfaces; a steel-wire brush to clean off caked mud, seed, and trash; decent, dry housing in the off season; and replacement of parts before they completely wear out, are ways to get many more years of life and better working results. If these practices are followed, the costs of being sole owner of crop-starting tools will not be excessive.

CULTIVATING TOOLS

There is usually no question whether or not cultivating tools should be owned by the individual farmer. The number of days-per-year usage is so high and the necessity of cultivating at precisely the right time—for weed-control or for laying corn by, for example —is so apparent that few farmers ever inquire whether there is any way to get this equipment without single ownership.

The prime consideration in cultivator selection, therefore, is not first cost but operating cost. You should discover the optimum range your power tools will permit and make use of it. Certainly there is no advantage or economy in cultivating two rows when your tractor will handle four without straining. Indeed, on large operations there is a strong trend to go to multi-rows. Since cultivation is usually vastly easier than soil preparation, the power unit that will strain to handle two-bottoms alone will more than likely walk away with a four-row cultivator.

More and more farmers are experimenting with combining several jobs into one operation. On some soils and in some areas it is perfectly feasible to hitch disk, spike tooth, drill, and roller all behind one power unit. Elsewhere it is not uncommon to cultivate and side-dress at the same time. Cultivation combined with dusting or spraying is another practical doubling-up operation.

At one time farmers believed that there were a number of reasons for cultivating. Not only weed control but moisture conservation, aerating the soil, and making plant nutrients more available were thought to be benefits. Today, however, weed control is generally recognized as the chief reason. If this premise is accepted, then it is in order to inquire whether mechanical uprooting of weeds is the only, or the best, way to dispose of them. In the case of cotton, for instance, mechanical weeding has had to be supplemented by hand hoeing. As long as this was necessary, the cost of cotton in this country stood in poor relationship to cost in other cotton-raising countries. However, if the weeds could be controlled by some fast, economical, mechanical method, we would be able to compete with the world price of cotton.

One answer to the problem is the flame-weeder. This device throws out flames of extremely high temperature which singe the weeds both in the row and between the rows. The sheath on the cotton plant protects it from the flame during the brief seconds it is passing by, but most weeds are not so protected if they are exposed to it when they are small enough and before they have turned woody. Experiments to date promise good results for this device, and the research workers in charge of its development expect it to be fully competent to handle, in addition to cotton, sugar cane and many other crops. One of its possibilities—that may make it useful for sugar beets, for example—requires a revolving hood attachment that permits the flame to hit the row only at stated intervals. Thus it seems logical to suppose that one day beet thinning may be done by flame rather than by hand or by a mechanical blocker.

Even more revolutionary is the modern way of weeding by chemicals. Weed killers have been known for a long time, but unfortunately they killed wanted plants as well as weeds and often left a lethal residue that would sterilize a field for several years. Now there is a hormone which kills a long list of weeds that infest lawns without harming the grass. This particular chemical, though, is death to clovers; hence its use is limited as far as most farming operations are concerned. But it is not at all impossible that further research will bring us a whole pharmacopoeia of cheap, easily applied weed killers that will supplant many present cultivation practices.

Here, again, mulch farming deserves mention. Potatoes, cut as for regular seed and laid on the ground, then covered with a heavy straw mulch, have been grown successfully. Great claims have been made for the yields and low costs of this operation. Other experiments in mulch farming are going on all over the country, one of the primary claims being that this system elim-

61

inates or drastically reduces the need for cultivation. Its proponents likewise make rather amazing statements on the concomitant moisture conservation. In some sections of the country, moreover, mulching has long been favored for both weed control and moisture conservation in orchards.

At this time, flame, chemical oil spray, and mulch weed-control methods cannot be said to be widely accepted in practice. Enough evidence is on hand, however, to warrant the recommendation that the farmer pursue the progress of work underway at various experiment stations, in the expectation that these methods may well be standard in tomorrow's agriculture. Forward-looking farmers will want to try out on a small scale some of these ideas. It should be remembered that almost any new development will need some modification for each individual farm. By experimenting now, the alert manager gets the jump on his competitors.

Finally, care of cultivating tools is just as important as that of tillage or seed-starting tools. Cultivator frames should be kept painted, working surfaces rust-proofed, and worn parts replaced. Winter is the time to buy and attach new scoops, shovels, sweeps, or rods.

WAR IMPLEMENTS

The topic of sprayers, dusters, and fumigators brings to the fore again the question of whether or not to own the equipment. In general there are the same reasons for owning it as for owning cultivating tools. When your crops need dusting or spraying, so will your neighbor's; thus you may not get a co-operatively owned machine when your need is greatest. Likewise, a custom man may be so scheduled that he cannot get around to your place when conditions are ideal for working on it.

On the other hand, there are few places in farming where size of rig reduces operating costs so dramatically. The new high-powered sprayers will do in a matter of hours work that would have taken days under the old methods. With hand pump or tank-and-auxiliary-pump rigs, a farm may need several hands primarily for pest control. When the original and rather high investment that equipment of this sort requires is considered—when operating cost, depreciation, needed hired labor, price of chemicals, replacement of hoses, spray tips, and general upkeep of rig is all added

The disk plow, such as this Doniphan County, Kansas, 10-foot model, running in widths up to 60 feet, is the favored ground breaker in the Plains country.

Flame-weeders, two-, four-, or even more-row models, are gaining increasing acceptance in the cotton South and are appearing in the North, particularly on contoured fields.

and divided by the acreage treated—the cost per acre looks frightening, especially since in some orchard regions ten sprayings per season are not unusual.

Phytophthora infestans is quite a jaw-breaking name. It is the name of the organism that caused the great Irish famine by destroying Ireland's potato crop in 1846. It has caused other uncounted millions of dollars' worth of damage by destroying potato crops in other places over many years. It is the organism that causes the plant disease known as late blight of potatoes. Plant pathologists have learned enough of its secrets and behavior to know how to control it, and now the farmer can protect his crops from its ravages by following their recommendations. But that is the new problem. The treatment involves spraying or dusting the crop with Bordeaux mixture from three to seven or eight times during the growing season, depending upon moisture conditions. Proper spraying or dusting requires expensive equipment.

This situation is merely an illustration, which could be many times repeated, of how one technical change in agriculture has brought another. Scientists found an answer to a serious plant-disease problem. Then engineers had to build the equipment by means of which the scientific findings could be practically applied. Now farmers have the problem of buying and using that equipment effectively.

When farmers first started spraying potatoes, they used small-sized inexpensive equipment. On two scores this equipment has proved unsatisfactory: First, it does not give as good control as more recently developed machines; and second, it is not fast enough, requiring too much labor per acre. Larger spray pumps have been developed that will deliver spray material under greater pressure and give better control; larger motors have been used to run them; larger spray tanks have been added to the machines to carry more material; and longer booms to cover more rows have been used on the larger rigs.

The grower with a large acreage of potatoes can afford a rig like this; in fact, he cannot afford not to have it. But the little grower is handicapped, just as he is in getting and using some other equipment items. Either he uses small equipment that requires more labor and runs up his production cost; or he manages to get larger equipment, operates with a high overhead per acre, and runs up his cost; or he raises his crop without spraying, which reduces his average yield and again runs up his cost. There are farm enterprises—potatoes are not the only one—where equipment improvements have resulted in exactly this sort of comparative position between the small-enterprise unit and the one that is enough larger to be able to carry more overhead.

Potato growing is a particularly good illustration of this situation. The crop is grown in small quantities on very large numbers of farms—many thousands of growers have only one or two acres, the potatoes being raised primarily for home use. Few of these acres are sprayed at all. Of course, the growers want the potatoes, but they are not dependent upon them for a living. They are not commercial producers. If a crop blights, they will get by just the same. Next year they will raise another acre on another piece of ground, where maybe blight will not show up.

Then there are the larger commercial growers, raising twenty to fifty acres or more. They can and do have up-to-date equipment and use it economically. It is the in-between growers, with four or five acres or even eight or ten, who are squeezed. Potatoes to them are a commercial enterprise, but they are hard pressed to get and use the proper equipment on an economical and competitive basis.

In some areas an answer to this particular difficulty has been worked out. S. W. Warren and L. B. Darrah have reported on the operations of ten potato-spraying rings in western New York, which, in that area at least, have been a very practical solution.[1] An average of thirty-eight growers per ring, with an average of seven acres of potatoes per grower, contracted with a ring operator to take over their potato spraying on a custom basis. With 266 acres to be sprayed, the operator was in a position to purchase efficient, high-capacity equipment with which to do the job, and then to furnish spraying service to the ring members at a very nominal fee per acre.

The new high-powered machines do such an effective job in such a short time that one in a neighborhood can literally supplant a dozen or more old-fashioned rigs. Accordingly, if you can hire such work done, it is more than likely that you will save

[1] S. W. Warren and L. B. Darrah, *Cost of Operating Potato Spray Rings* (New York State College of Agriculture Mimeographed Bulletin AE 478, 1944).

money. When it comes to bloc airplane or helicopter dusting, there is no argument. If there is not a sufficient acreage of the particular crop needing the service in your neighborhood, it might be well to pause and reconsider whether growing that crop is best for you. Necessary investment in war implements is so high that the farmer expecting to grow crops that need extensive spraying or dusting should think twice unless custom service is available or his acreage is large enough to justify the expense of equipment ownership. In any case he should not expect to cut corners in pest control and stay in the orchard, truck-crop, or cotton business.

The newest method in pest control will bear close attention. It is soil fumigation. Previously, a Scottish grower found excellent results in truck-crop production despite his unfavorable climate and the presence in catastrophic quantities of soil microorganisms such as nematodes. He combatted the poor climatic conditions by heating his soil, using a very expensive network of steam pipes. Prices for fresh green crops in his market justified the expense. But soil pests hampered his operation seriously; therefore he turned to soil sterilization with steam. He was successful.

During the war, soil sterilization began to receive serious attention in the western United States. Steam has been used but not in a pipe-network system. Rather, portable steam units were developed which moved across the fields killing the unwanted soil pests as they traveled. Several other ideas were tried out, but the one that seems to offer most promise is the use of the chemical D-D, a description of which appears below.

"D-D (WITHOUT THE T) Before farmers have had a chance to find out whether DDT will do all the things they hope it will, they may have a chance to use another chemical aid to agriculture recently announced by the Shell Union Oil Corp., San Francisco, California. This product is a soil fumigant designed to stop the depredations of soil parasites, particularly plant nematodes (a vicious form of microscopic worm), wireworms, and garden centipedes. These insects attack with costly results pineapples, carrots, sugar beets, lettuce, beans, tomatoes, peppers, eggplants, cucumbers, melons, cotton, potatoes, and alfalfa.

"Although the farmer has long sprayed, dusted, and fumigated the pests that attack plants aboveground, he has been help-less against subsurface microscopic life. Most farmers still do not know that such pests exist. Yet they have been so ravenous that in some areas in England potatoes can be grown on the same plot of ground only once in seven years. In some parts of Utah, sugar beets can be planted only once in four years. In the intervening years, plants that resist the parasites must be grown so the subsurface population will die down. If D-D lives up to expectations (it is still under experiment and test), it will raise yields, reduce plant mortality, and permit shorter rotations.

"Although the bulk of the 1945 production is going to Hawaii, it is planned to have D-D available for national distribution, both to victory gardeners and to farmers, in 1946. Gardeners can apply the fumigant by spot injection tools now used for weed control. For large users there is a special machine that adjusts the dosage to the type of soil and the variety of parasites. The amount required varies from 200 to 400 pounds per acre. The cost is 11½ cents per pound, f.o.b. Houston, Texas.

"The special machine is the Shell-developed application cart . . . Shell estimates it will cost $400, less if quantity production is possible. Besides selling the applicator and the insecticide direct, Shell will offer an 'in the ground' service, now being tested in California, whereby the company furnishes the machine, the D-D, and an operator at a cost of 20 cents per pound of fumigant up to 200 pounds per acre. Above 200 pounds, the cost drops to 17½ cents. The farmer furnishes only the tractor. The equipment fumigates around twenty acres per day, depending on the depth necessary for sterilization.

"How many millions of dollars in crops this new chemical may save is anybody's guess, but it is certain to be large in the South, Southwest, and California. Actually nematodes have been found as far north as New York, Michigan, and the state of Washington. One possible use that the experimenters have not yet claimed is the fumigation of poultry and swine ranges. At present, poultry and swine must be kept off used ground for two to four years to avoid soil diseases, due largely to the animal nematodes. D-D may eliminate this pasture waste and give the livestockmen the help it promises to give the crop men."[2]

2 Reprinted from The Farm Column, *Fortune,* October, 1945, 180, reprinted by courtesy of the publisher of *Fortune.*

In concluding the topic of war implements, the authors prophesy that custom work will come more and more to be the standard practice in pest control. Either a large grower will own and operate the necessary machines for his own and a neighbor's benefit, or a custom specialist will do the job for a whole community. Only the largest growers will operate their own equipment for their sole benefit. These trends are now strong and growing speedily in California, Arizona, South Texas, the cotton South, and Florida. They are beginning to make an appearance in the Northeast and the fruit-and-truck-growing Pacific Northwest. It may be only tomorrow that the Corn Belt will control the borer by large-scale custom work.

HARVESTING TOOLS

Harvesting tools belong to the category in which the war between sole ownership and outside ownership of tools began. Tillage tools may be used twice or several times a year, depending upon the region. There are spring plowing and fall plowing, ditching, terracing, irrigation, and many other jobs that keep tillage tools fairly busy. Fall seeding gives more than once-a-year usage to crop-starting tools. Cultivators and war implements are used for a full season and sometimes more. But big, expensive harvesting tools—such as grain, pea, and bean threshers, combines, hay presses, and more recently the cotton picker—get a very few days' work a year, depreciation is heavy, upkeep is high, and operating economies often do not offset fixed charges. Consequently, long ago, the itinerant thresher appeared in the Palouse country of Washington, the Bread Basket of Kansas, and the Panhandle of Texas.

Later, the portable combine made the thresher obsolete on big operations, although small operators were still dependent upon the steam engine and bulky separator. The binder (not an expensive machine) and custom threshing seemed a very good compromise, particularly where it was desired to save straw for bedding or mulch. Then came the one-man combine with cutter-bar lengths as low as four, five, or six feet. It seemed that the problem was solved very satisfactorily; i.e., big sixteen-foot or larger combines for big operations, little four- to ten-foot combines for more modest operations. And as the "all-purpose" feature had been added, the first cost did not seem too far out of line.

67

Then the war came, man power disappeared, and threshing machines for the most part were old and decrepit, while there simply were not enough combines in the grain belt to get in the bumper crops. Into this heaven-sent opportunity for a promotionally minded equipment maker stepped the Canadian-American house of Massey-Harris. The company proposed, if priorities were granted, to manufacture five hundred of its self-propelled combines, organize a harvesting army, start the army from Texas, and work it north to or beyond the Canadian border, getting in a guaranteed million acres of grain by custom work. The success of the plan is now history. Most, if not all the men who bought the combines paid for them in the two war years they did custom work. Some made the whole price in the first year. Thus, at least five hundred custom operators in the Grain Belt were in business, and safely financed, by the end of hostilities.

Of course, five hundred custom operators cannot begin to handle America's harvest needs. But they make a more than sufficient sample to point the way toward the probable picture of the future. The ultimate pattern in the Grain Belt may look something like this:

A custom operator, using large Diesel-powered and multi-bottomed gang plows—perhaps as high as twelve- or sixteen-bottoms or a like number of one-ways, with disks and harrows hitched in tandem behind the plows—will move on a grain farmer's place. For a cost much less over the long term than that which the farmer would have to meet in order to own his own implements, the custom operator will fit seedbed and plant the grain crop. As in the harvest time, he will work from south to north so that he catches the best planting time in each community. Then in late summer, he will return with his big self-propelled combines and harvest the crop. The owner will have nothing to do but sign contracts, take out hail insurance, and collect his elevator receipts after a regular trucker has hauled the combined grain to railhead.

A picture of this sort seems to spell the end of the family farm in its traditional raiment as far as the Grain Belt is concerned. It is not likely, however, that the pattern will become widespread so long as thousands of grain farmers have their own machinery, though a stiff decline in grain prices might speed acceptance of the system. A continued difficulty in getting farm labor at reason-

68

able wage rates would also turn some owners to considering the proposition.

It is quite likely that the new sugar-beet harvester may not be owned widely by growers. The sugar refiners have traditionally financed the crop, secured seed and labor for the growers, then contracted for the output. It would be only carrying on an accepted relationship if the refiners owned and operated the expensive sugar-beet harvesters.

None but the largest and best-financed cotton planters can afford any of the several new cotton harvesters. The capacity of the machines is such that a very large acreage is necessary to justify the capital investment.[3] In addition, airplane dusting to defoliate the crop is desirable where the mechanical pickers are used, to keep trash out of the lint and raise the grading. This seems to indicate that small growers will have to utilize custom or big neighbor operators, for if domestic cotton prices decline to world levels, the only way to stay in business is by getting the large savings of mechanical harvesting over hand picking.

Undoubtedly as more and more progress is made in perfecting harvesting machines for a wide variety of crops, some of which until only yesterday no one believed could be mechanically harvested, great changes in farming patterns will result. When harvesting costs are cut for big operators, the small operator harvesting by hand methods is put at an impossible competitive disadvantage. Up to a point he may sell his labor for nothing in order to stay in business. Then, if surpluses appear and prices weaken, the machines stay inexorably in business while the hand operator uses his capital for operation and ultimately goes bankrupt.

What has this mordant thought to do with the consideration of your harvest machinery? Simply this: Except on the Great Plains, the huge ranches of California and Texas, and the large-scale plantations of the South, there is not likely to be a time within the near future when seedbed-fitting costs are reduced so drastically by further big-scale mechanization as to offer a threat to you if you are a small operator. However, you can probably compete in cultivation. Already in many a community—and there will be more tomorrow—you can get the advantage of big-scale spraying, dust-

---

[3] As we go to press, a small cotton picker is announced which may be low enough in cost to permit wide ownership by small-acreage growers.

ing, and fumigating machines. But when you come to harvesting—usually a high unit-cost operation and often, now or in the past, a hand operation—there is a definite competitive threat to the small-scale farmer from the big operator.

Examine your money crops and their probable future internationally. From a farming standpoint, we have, in truth, reached a "One World" status. Can you produce your chosen crop to meet probable world prices? If not, will your operation and your finances permit you to invest in harvesting (or other) equipment to an extent that your costs will drop to a competitive level? If you can afford the purchase of an expensive harvesting machine, will your acreage justify it? If not, can you be the first in your neighborhood to acquire the machine and contract with your neighbors to do their work before someone else gets the same idea? If you can not afford a machine, your acreage will not justify it, and whatever custom arrangements seem likely still will not get you under the wire, here is the place to stop and consider whether or not you should switch your entire farm plan.

Perhaps you may feel that your particular crop is under no threat from harvesting machines-to-come. For instance, you may own a peach orchard. You feel that you can compete with anyone else any place because everybody has to hire pickers just as you do. But—in California an experimental peach picker is in development. Or maybe tomatoes are your money crop. Again, in California, an experimental machine using the electric eye is harvesting the crop by color wanted. And walnuts and prunes are now "picked" by machine.

Maybe your most important field crop is forage. You can not afford competitively to make hay in the old way, particularly if you are in a humid region. To meet the competition of other forage producers, you must anticipate the investment of goodly capital in a forage harvester or a pickup baler, and possibly a mow-curing installation. It is true that these machines are going into custom operation very rapidly. One young engineer is even trying to perfect a portable hay dryer with the idea of marketing it to neighborhood haying rings.

Whatever the crop, find out what is ahead for it as far as harvesting is concerned. The farm press, your county agent, or your state extension engineer can answer your questions. Next, find out if you can get the benefits of the new or proposed machines through custom operation or co-operative ownership if the selling price promises to be too high to be justified by the size of your operation. (*Note:* All new harvesting machines are not necessarily big-capacity, high-cost machines, but the general trends are toward that type.)

The time to figure harvest costs is before planting, not after reaping. Therefore, this point in our pencil-and-paper figuring on equipment management is the place to pause and work out costs by crop. Perhaps the original crop plan is wrong economically, even though soil type is right for the crop chosen, and even though there is enough money on hand to buy machines without going into a dangerous debt situation. For example, there are many lands in the East where wheat will grow well, with no more threat from rust and smut than elsewhere. A grower could well afford to buy a combine to harvest the crop. But can he grow that wheat as cheaply as he can buy western wheat at his dealer's? Actual experience in many cases has shown that buying a crop grown a thousand miles away is a better bet than growing it.

Only too many farmers state, and they are correct, that they can fit seedbed, plant, cultivate (if necessary), and get as good a crop on the stalk or vine as any farmer anywhere else. Though they are right up to this point, can they get that crop to crib, barn, granary, or packing house for the same cost that farmers elsewhere can? If so, then the difference in transportation charges may make the crop a good one. However, more often than not, highly mechanized harvesting in some other area permits that grower to get in his crop, ship it long distances, and still beat the local grower. (For instance, a Kansas wheat man usually can beat the costs of a New York state wheat grower when the Kansan is getting a twenty-two bushel yield and the New York state man is doing forty or fifty bushels. A big part of the difference is cost of harvesting.)

A crop in the field is virtually worthless unless it is disposed of at the right time. As nutritional studies progress, this becomes more evident every day. Hay that is now top in carotene content may one day be graded down drastically as against what will then be No. 1. Tomatoes ripened on the vine have from four to eight times more vitamin C than those picked green and ripened in packing house or in transit. This might argue well for growers close to northern metropolises except that air freight may give the edge to the grower who has the greatest number of sunny days per year. Corn that does not get a chance to dent and have its moisture content reduced is useless in trade. Thus, if you are in a region where the corn season is liable to be curtailed at either end by frosts, you are in a bad competitive condition. If added to this handicap, the natural corn region—the Corn Belt—is completely mechanized, your situation is really perilous. Farmers there will take off their corn with a four-row picker, or a husker-shredder, at a fraction of your cost, for they will be harvesting large acreage with large-capacity machines.

To the other considerations of harvest machinery, add the item of probable nutritional grading as one of tomorrow's price conditioners. That means that to meet the competition of the future, harvesting will have to be as finely timed as animal breeding. Next week or the week after will not do. The man who gets the best price will be the one who is so equipped, or so served by custom work, that he can harvest by stop watch rather than by almanac. Some farmers are going to get that best price. They will be the good managers who have matched proper soil types, proper machinery, and proper crop choice to reach market at the time of optimum prices with highest-quality goods. And their harvesting machinery probably will be the key to their success.

9. Power Units

TO plow a 40-acre corn field six inches deep involves moving and turning 30,000 tons of soil. This job well illustrates the function of power on the farm. If the farmer should do the work himself with a spade, it would require 400 days of extremely heavy work and the farmer would have to lift and invert 75 tons of soil a day. Even using a plodding yoke of oxen pulling a twelve-inch plow would enable him to accomplish as much in one day as he could with a spade in ten days.

Five horses on two fourteen-inch plows will turn 40 acres in eight days. A modern tractor on two sixteen-inch bottoms will clean up the job in four days; or using four bottoms at four miles per hour will do it in a day and a half. Thus, with animal power, and still more with mechanical power, the farmer can multiply his own work accomplishment many times over.

In reverse, this means that a farmer sells his labor more and more cheaply the farther down the power ladder he goes. Net returns for labor are in proportion to accomplishment less the cost of power and equipment used. Farmers as a whole are rapidly shifting toward higher-capacity tools because the increase in accomplishment is greater than the increase in cost (except, of course, where capital outlay and annual carrying costs for tools are extended to an uneconomical extreme).

Mechanical power has already replaced half the horses and mules kept on United States farms a quarter-century ago. More and better tractors to come most surely will decrease horse numbers still further. Farm-management services, farm cost accountants, much of the farm press, and practically all other agencies who have analyzed the comparative costs have given support to this switch in power units.

Though the weight of the evidence favors tractors, horses still have their supporters. Horses, it is claimed, may be farm raised and may be fed from the farm. Although, if purchased, the number of horses to equal a tractor's power may involve as much cash outlay as the purchase of a tractor, the cash expense for maintaining the animals is much less. Several horses may be hitched together for heavy draft jobs, or used singly or in pairs for lighter work. Thus horse power may be more flexible than tractor power. Horse equipment is invariably less expensive than its tractor-designed counterpart. Horses produce manure to aid in soil maintenance. And finally, some farmhands are good teamsters but not good mechanics.

Tractors, on the other hand, require no fuel and little care when not in use. On an annual basis a tractor requires about half as much time for maintenance as one horse and about one-tenth as much as five horses, thus leaving time which the farmer may use for additional productive work. Though tractors require cash expense for fuel, parts, and replacements that cannot be farm produced, tractors may accomplish much more work per dollar of total expense. They may be worked long hours: twenty-four hours a day and days on end, if necessary, by working drivers in shifts with lights at night. They require no land for feed crops, thus automatically permitting more products to be sold as an offset to the greater cash costs. By their greater speed they have decreased direct labor hours per acre. They have reduced seasonal labor peaks on many jobs and in this manner also have raised the ceiling on labor accomplishment. They have boosted yields and cut crop losses by permitting more timely planting, cultivating, and harvesting. They are preferred by today's hired hands. They help to keep farmers' sons on the farm.

Early tractors, those of World War I vintage and thereabouts, were suitable mainly for heavy drawbar work such as plowing and fitting and for belt work, leaving many other jobs on the farm for which horses were more efficient. As has been explained previously, the principal handicap to the versatility of early tractors was a lack of equipment designed specifically for use with them. In 1915 one tractor company published a pamphlet promoting the 8–15 horsepower tractor it was then producing. Much of the pamphlet was devoted to methods of hitching farm tools to the tractor, but most of the tools shown were those already common on farms and designed for horse operation.

Changes in tractors and tractor equipment since 1915 have increased their versatility, dependability, and speed. Tractor history comprises fitting the machine for more and more specific jobs, leaving fewer and fewer power needs for which the horse has any advantage. The introduction of the tricycle-type (general-purpose) tractor in the early twenties and the improvements in it since have given great impetus to horseless farming.

Because each farm differs from all others, it should not be concluded without question that every farmer should replace his horses with tractor power. When a manager sits down to figure the relative merits of the two on his own farm, he has to find answers to questions such as these: If he buys a tractor, will he still need to keep horses? (From a profit point of view this should be answered honestly, not sentimentally. Many who think they need horses could get by very well and with much less expense without them.) If he has to keep horses anyway, would the duplication of power units make any worthwhile saving possible? Even if tractor power would cost more, would he be able to save enough labor so that power, equipment, and labor costs combined would represent a significant saving? Can he afford the extra investment that tractor power and equipment would require? Can he successfully meet the cash costs of tractor operation? Does he have the kind of help on the farm that is capable of using from eight to fifteen hundred dollars' worth of high-speed, mechanical equipment in the field? From the cost-of-production angle can he afford not to have a tractor?

In spite of all recognized advantages of the tractor, it must be noted that some farms can stay in business with horses but will go out of business if mechanized. It is true that the operators of these farms will be selling their own labor at close to coolie wages; but the potential production of these places is so limited that even machines cannot help. Technological advances of any kind serve only those farms which are adaptable to the new development.

Some farm lands are too rough, too stony, and too inherently infertile to justify the expense of modern machines. Anyone who has tried to use fast mechanized equipment on badly cut-up, small hillside farms knows what a heartbreaking and pocketbook-straining job it is. However, these acreages can produce a livelihood of a sort. Horses can utilize the forage on rough pastures. A few acres can be set aside on the gentler slopes for oats. Hay and silage (raised by animal power) with pasture can provide sufficient forage to maintain a small livestock operation.

Here is an example of what happens when a farm not adapted to mechanization is equipped with expensive machinery. In the late nineteen thirties a farm in the Allegheny Plateau country was handsomely equipped with a brand-new line of tools, including combine, hay baler, tractor, and the common field machinery. Pasture, hay, small grains, and dairy cows were raised; but the soil was such that, in local parlance, "the hard pan came up to the second rail in the fence."

At normal planting time, the fields were almost always too wet to work. During the growing season the soil was too dry for good crop growth. Vegetation on the meadows and pastures was usually thin and poor. The cattle showed the roughness and poverty to be expected.

Three years later the owner liquidated the small equity he had left and quit farming. There were two hundred acres of cropland and pasture in the farm. But acreage alone, as his experience demonstrates, does not tell the whole story on equipment justification. The high cash expense of his equipment broke this farmer. With horses he might have made out, for on farms such as this an operator can be successful only on the expenses he does not have.

Well-laid-out farms with high-yielding soils are the ones where mechanized power comes into its own, where the cash costs of tractor farming are met most successfully, and where the advantages of tractors are most fully realized. In 1944 a place answering these requirements was inspected. Two men were plowing: one with three horses on a fourteen-inch walking plow, plowing at the rate of three acres a day; one on a tractor with two fourteen-inch plow bottoms, plowing about eight acres a day. The account books provided the information for the following comparison:

With Horses	
30 horse hours @ 25¢	$ 7.50
10 man hours @ 50¢	5.00
Equipment use, 3 acres @ 20¢	.60
Total per 10-hour day	$13.10
Cost per acre plowed	$ 4.37
With Tractor	
10 tractor hours @ 60¢	$ 6.00
10 man hours @ 50¢	5.00
Equipment use, 8 acres @ 45¢	3.60
Total per 10-hour day	$14.60
Cost per acre plowed	$ 1.83

The cost per day was greater with the tractor, but it is significant that comparative accomplishment cut the cost per acre with the tractor to 40 per cent of the cost with horses. Moreover, when the expense was figured on a per-acre basis, the teamster alone cost more than tractor and driver combined. As farm wage rates continue their long-time upward trend, this sort of comparison becomes increasingly pertinent. Many farmers who own both horses and tractor are using the horses fewer days each year, simply because they cannot afford to pay going wage rates for a man to follow a team.

At many power jobs the difference in horse and tractor accomplishment is not so great as in plowing. Yet there are few jobs indeed at which the tractor is not faster. The lesson which the above figures most forcefully point out is that savings in the combined power and labor cost per unit of work provide the advantage of tractor farming.

D. Howard Doane says: "Even when horse power is free, I can't afford to use it. I made this discovery on a Midwestern grass farm I bought in the early 30's, where I kept from four to six mares for raising mule colts for sale.

"My horse power was free, because sale of my young mules paid all of the expenses of keeping this stock.

"That was back in 1933, when labor was plentiful at 15¢ per hour. But 1947 isn't 1933! The price of mules is down 50% to 75%. Feed is up. Most important, labor costs four times what it did 12 years ago. Also a cow or steer which now takes the place of a brood mare on pasture, is making more money than the mares and colts ever did.

"When I added this all up, I bought a tractor in 1946. . . .

"The big saving is in labor. We made a test on moving a heavy self-feeder. First, the driver got his tractor out of the shed; went through two gates; drove more than 1100 feet; moved the feeder 30 feet, and then drove back to the shed.

"Then he repeated the job with a team, getting them out of their stables, harnessing them, doing the moving, and returning. The job took 9 minutes with the tractor; 32 minutes with the team. . . .

"We tested mowing, fencing, and other jobs. All pointed the same way.

"If there is a last stronghold for horse power, it should be a grass farm. But I've tried it, and I, too, must add my farewell to the faithful horse."[1]

Divergent trends have been evident in recent years in tractor and equipment size. Small units have been developed for small-acreage farms. On the other hand, larger tools, such as four-row corn planters and cultivators, have come increasingly into use. These particular machines require a somewhat larger tractor than is employed with standard two-row corn equipment, and therefore have their place in a heavier line of tools. What size should an individual farmer purchase? As always, the answer must be deter-

[1] D. Howard Doane, "Horse vs. Tractor," *Farm Journal,* March, 1947, 69.

mined in relation to his own operations and on the basis of comparative costs and savings to him. Here is an example of calculations by which such an answer may be found.

Data from several studies of equipment on Corn Belt farms[2] have made possible comparisons of the labor, power, and equipment costs involved in raising and harvesting forty acres of corn with horse equipment and with tractor equipment of two sizes. In horse operations it has been assumed that multiple hitches would be used whenever possible to speed up the accomplishment of one man—for example, five horses on a plow with two fourteen-inch bottoms, five horses on a ten-foot disk, three horses on a two-row cultivator, and so on. The tractor tools considered are the sizes commonly used with the two-plow and three-plow tractors. The equipment investment was calculated at the approximate price of new machinery at the beginning of the war. (*See* table page 79.)

Labor requirements per acre with the two-row tractor equipment and a mechanical picker are only 45 per cent of those with horse-drawn equipment and hand picking; with four-row equipment, only one-third as much. The lowest equipment costs, by far, are with horse-drawn tools. When the power, equipment, and labor costs are totaled—and it is the total that is the payoff—a slight advantage rests with the tractor equipment even on a forty-acre unit of operation. And in favor of the four-row over the two-row tools, this comparison shows a twenty-five-cent-per-acre difference. No very important decision can be influenced by twenty-five cents an acre. In fact, probably few farmers would want the additional investment in four-row equipment—a total difference of $550—if it would save so little.

But the comparison should not be dropped at this point. If the capacity of each line of equipment is figured at the corn acreage that may be produced with the same number of hours of labor,

2 J. Brownlee Davidson and S. Milton Henderson, *Life, Service, and Cost of Service of Farm Machines on 400 Iowa Farms* (Iowa Bulletin P. 37, 1942); Claude K. Shedd, Edgar V. Collins, and J. Brownlee Davidson, *Labor, Power, and Machinery in Corn Production* (Iowa Bulletin 365, 1937); Wylie D. Goodsell, *Cost and Utilization of Power and Labor on Iowa Farms* (Iowa Research Bulletin 258, 1939); Frank Miller, W. L. Ruden, and C. W. Smith, *Cost of Tractor Power on Nebraska Farms* (Nebraska Agricultural Experiment Station Bulletin 324, 1939); Frank Miller and W. L. Ruden, *Cost of Operating Machinery on Nebraska Farms* (Nebraska Agricultural Experiment Station Bulletin 366, 1944).

Labor, Power, and Equipment Requirements to Produce 40 Acres of Corn

	Horses and horse-drawn equipment	"2-plow" general purpose tractor with 2-row planter-and cultivator	"3-plow" general purpose tractor with 4-row planter and cultivator
Time Required:			
Labor up to harvest time, hours	380	180	120
Power use to harvest time,			
Horse hours	1,300	——	——
Tractor hours	——	180	120
Labor for harvesting, hours			
Hand snapping	200	——	——
Machine picking	——	80	80
Power use for harvesting,			
Horse hours	400	——	——
Tractor hours	——	80	80
Investment in:			
Power	$750	$ 900	$1,200
Equipment	450	1,850	2,100
Costs:			
Power cost,			
Horses at 12¢ per hour	$204	——	——
Tractors at 50¢ and 60¢	——	$130	$120
Annual equipment cost, Figured at 12% of purchase price	54	222	252
Labor cost, Figured at 50¢ an hour	290	130	100
Total power, equipment, and labor cost	548	482	472
Power, equipment, and labor cost per acre	13.70	12.05	11.80

then the two-row equipment can handle 85 acres and the four-row equipment 127 acres, against 40 acres for the horse operation. In each case 580 hours of labor would be used. The comparative performance of the three lines of equipment is then as follows:

79

	Horses and horse-drawn equipment	"2-plow" general purpose tractor and 2-row equipment	"3-plow" general purpose tractor and 4-row equipment
Acres of corn that could be handled with same hours of labor	40	85	127
Total power and equipment cost	$258	$498	$570
Labor cost	290	290	290
Total	$548	$788	$860
Labor, power and equipment cost per acre	13.70	9.27	6.77
Bushels of corn produced (60-bushel yield)	2400	5100	7620
Labor, power and equipment cost per bushel	23¢	15¢	11¢
Minutes of labor per bushel	14.5	6.8	4.6

Corn production per hour of labor in this comparison is thirteen bushels with the four-row-tractor equipment against nine bushels with the two-row and four bushels with the horses. The direct costs of production are only half as great with the high-speed equipment as with horse operation. Other costs, mainly seed and land costs, presumably would be about the same in each case.

Probably the most important fact brought out by these comparisons is the relative size of farms that can be operated with the different lines of machinery. In the central Corn Belt, 40 acres of corn on 80 acres of cropland is more the rule than the exception. Accepting this relationship, the same labor force could as easily operate 240 acres of cropland with four-row-tractor equipment as it could 80 acres with horse-drawn tools.

The significant point is that a line of mechanical equipment has the capacity to handle more acreage than the horse equipment, while the labor force remains unchanged. If the equipment is not used to operate the greater acreage that it makes possible, the owner has equipped himself out of part of his job, unless he makes other changes in his farm business. True, he may make as much net income from half as much work on corn, and he may use the saving in time to read books (like this one), or to go fishing, as he prefers. Or he may use the equipment to operate more land, cut down his overhead per acre and per bushel, and strengthen his competitive position in relation to other producers. Tools and machines that are used at less than capacity result in a higher overhead cost per unit of production.

How about tractors on small farms? The opinion has been common that the "little" farm cannot make profitable use of tractor power and equipment because of the relation of investment required to usage. An answer must be determined for each farm separately—and the question of how small must be considered.

Here is a one-man dairy farm. The operator has been farming with one team of horses for which he has about 550 hours of use annually—mostly for hauling manure, harvesting twenty-five acres of hay, and producing about five acres each of oats and corn for silage. His team is getting old and soon must be replaced. Using information on comparative costs obtained from agricultural experiment stations, he made an analysis which has been summarized (in the table on page 82) directly from his calculations.

His conclusion is that it will be to his advantage to buy a tractor of one-plow size instead of a replacement team of horses. His power and equipment investment will be boosted $750, which will increase depreciation and interest charges. Annual cash-out-of-pocket costs will increase by the excess of gas, oil, and repairs over present costs of horseshoeing and a little purchased grain. But total annual costs of power and equipment will be about sixty dollars lower with the tractor.

In addition to these differences, the tractor will free him from about one hundred hours of the time he now spends caring for his horses and approximately another two hundred hours in the field —time which he can use to advantage on his cows and hens. Disposal of the horses will leave an additional six tons of hay for the cattle, enough for two more cows and one heifer, a particularly important consideration because the farm is now so heavily stocked that roughage requirements have to be figured very closely. These factors plus the saving in annual cost are far more significant than the fact that hourly power costs will be ten cents higher with the tractor.

With his tractor this farmer could operate more land with

little or no additional help. However, since at present more land is not available to him, his decision to buy the tractor has been based entirely upon its use on his present small acreage and upon the considerations here presented. Many other farmers would have to take account of different conditions than those which have influenced this man's decision. Yet anyone who figures out his problems so carefully is not apt to make a serious mistake.

	Two horses and no tractor	A one-plow tractor and no horses
Annual use	550 team hours	325 hours
Investment:		
Two replacement horses	$300	—
Tractor	—	$800
Field equipment	680*	930**
Total	$980	$1,730
Annual cost:		
Equipment	$ 82	$ 112
Power:		
Depreciation	25	65
Interest	15	40
Housing	10	6
Labor	70	18
Feed	150	—
Fuel, oil, repairs	—	70
Miscellaneous (including shoeing and harness for horses)	25	6
	$295	$ 205
Total power and equipment	$377	$ 317
Power cost per hour of use	54¢	64¢

* His present inventory of field equipment.
** Present inventory plus items that will have to be added with the change to tractor power.

The surest way to get low-cost power on a farm is to have enough use for a tractor that overhead costs will be cut to a minimum. In Illinois it was found that depreciation, interest, housing, and insurance amounted to forty cents an hour on tractors used only 250 hours a year. When usage was increased to over 700 hours, these unavoidable overhead charges were reduced to thirteen cents an hour.[3] Obviously the farmer who is going to overcome the high capital costs of mechanized farming must get nearly full use out of his tools. It may mean more acres, or more intensively farmed acres, or a fuller line of tools with which more jobs may be done with tractor power. It may mean all these adjustments if the farmer's competitive position is to be most enhanced.

10. Depreciation: the Joker in Mechanization

NOBODY paid much attention to replacement costs when all the tools on a farm could be bought for a few hundred dollars. Once the farmer had a good team of horses, enough colts would be coming along to take over the work when the original team was too old. Modern power tools, however, do not reproduce themselves. Somewhere along the line, the owner has to set aside part of income to take care of replacing equipment that has been made obsolete by new developments or has just worn out.

Possibly you will do as too many farmers do. You will ignore annual charge-offs. They are only a bookkeeping item, anyway, you will tell yourself. When you need to replace anything, you will get it "on just one good year." That plan may work for awhile, but it is dangerous. In any event, before you invest in equipment is the time to take depreciation into full consideration, even though you neglect to do so subsequently. First consider how you can avoid depreciation entirely.

Many tools on many farms, items in which considerable money is invested, stand in the shed (or under the apple tree) year after year, to be used only a few hours or a few days each season. How much this sort of investment is justified every manager must decide for his own operation. To what extent is the convenience worth the cost? To what extent could tools be rented, or exchanged, or custom hired to cut down such overhead?

Many a farmer has bought certain equipment (or sometimes larger equipment than his own operations would justify) with the intention of using it in part for custom work. At the present time,

[3] P. E. Johnston, *Tractor Costs* (Illinois Agricultural Experiment Station AE 1318, 1940), 4.

combines, corn pickers, and field balers are machines frequently worked in this manner. Some important considerations are involved in a decision to buy equipment with this use in mind: (1) What is the probable volume of custom work to be done within a practical distance from home? (2) How many other men are offering custom service, or what are the prospects that farmers now employing it will buy their own machines? (3)Will the prevailing rate for custom work hold, or may it sink below a profitable figure if more machines come into use? (4) Will there be time during a short harvest season to get a profitable volume of business? (5) Will the pressure of farm work at home permit the custom operator to get away at the proper season without loss on his own farm? And (6) will the income from custom work be sufficient to pay for the labor used, the direct operating expenses of the equipment, and the loss of equipment value through depreciation?

Whatever way you look, you or someone else must face this matter of depreciation. If the equipment line is to be maintained on the farm, depreciation is as much an expense of use as the gas, oil, and grease for operation. Hertel and Williamson found that depreciation amounted to approximately 10 per cent of the inventory value of a general line of farm equipment (power equipment not included) on central New York farms, and to 44 per cent of the total annual cost of using and maintaining the equipment. For tractors, depreciation was 13 per cent of the inventory value and 28 per cent of the annual operating cost.[1]

Equipment depreciation may be figured in various ways. One way is the so-called "straight-line" method, by which a fixed percentage of the purchase price is subtracted from the value each year. This method results in a declining value which, when charted on graph paper, shows a straight-line decrease from the purchase price to a junk value at the time when the tool is expected to be worn out.

Another method of figuring depreciation is what is known as the "present-worth" system, which involves the determination of a sum of money that, if set aside each year and allowed to bear interest at a specified rate, will accumulate a sufficient total to replace the equipment at the end of a certain number of years. Deprecia-

[1] J. P. Hertel and Paul Williamson, *Costs of Farm Power and Equipment* (Cornell Agricultural Experiment Station Bulletin 751, 1941).

tion figured in this manner is small during the first years and becomes greater as the machinery grows older.

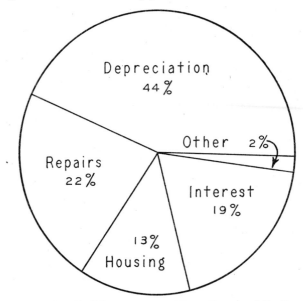

From Hertel and Williamson, *Costs of Farm Power and Equipment*, 19.

*Relative Importance of Various Cost Items Involved
in Maintaining Field Machinery*

The repair bills—money-out-of-pocket expenses—are the most obvious items; but the other expenses are there just the same. They are
all costs and must be met eventually if the farm equipment is to be
maintained.

A third method is known as "constant-percentage" depreciation, meaning that a constant percentage of the current inventory
value is deducted each year. For example, a machine may be calculated to be worth at the end of each year 80 per cent of its value
at the beginning of the year. If the plan is followed consistently, the
item would be depreciated to 14 per cent of its cost at the end of
ten years, and the annual depreciation would be heaviest in the
early years of the machine's life and become smaller with passing
time. This method usually comes closer to reflecting the current
resale value of equipment than the other methods.

The main point, after all, is not for a farmer to become involved in the theoretical methods by which depreciation may be figured, but simply to recognize that it is part of equipment cost and must be allowed for if his operating costs are to be properly charged and if his equipment is to be maintained.

A common method farmers use to reduce depreciation expense —and other equipment overhead—is to buy secondhand tools. They are less expensive than new tools, the annual interest charge on the investment is proportionately less, and, because they are partly depreciated when purchased, the annual depreciation is therefore less. Secondhand equipment is far more common on farms than is generally realized. Hertel and Williamson found that 45 per cent of the individual equipment items on the New York farms that they studied in 1936 had been purchased secondhand.

"One of the most common arguments against the use of second-hand tools is that they are unreliable. This argument would be more logical if all the second-hand tools that were available were those that other farmers were selling because they no longer worked satisfactorily. On the contrary, most second-hand tools are purchased at farm auctions, where they are sold, not because they are unsatisfactory, but because the operator has died or is quitting the farm. The farmer who buys his equipment new and wears it out is using the equivalent of second-hand equipment most of the time. Second-hand tools offered for sale may be in any condition. Some may be almost new, others very old; some may be in good repair, while others may need repairs that can be made at a reasonable cost; and still others may be beyond repair. Good judgment is required to buy second-hand tools that will be serviceable without paying too much for them."[2]

In order to hold equipment investment at a minimum and to have at the same time a reasonably complete line of tools, the purchase of some secondhand items is good management, particularly in the case of equipment that is used infrequently. The buyer should be careful that such machinery is dependable, that it will economically do the job for which it is bought, and that it is not overpriced in comparison with the cost of new equipment. Gen-

[2] Hertel and Williamson, *Costs of Farm Power and Equipment*, 26.

erally the rather simple tools with relatively few moving parts are the safest gambles for secondhand purchase. Complicated machines and those that can be easily damaged by abuse are more of a speculation when their former care is not known.

There is another matter that we will dogmatically say no farmer can afford to ignore—the care he gives his equipment after he has bought it will be a major factor in the length of its useful life, in the dependability of its service, and in the all-round satisfaction it will give. This is one of the most, if not the most, important ways to overcome depreciation.

The blacksmiths whose shops a short time ago were prominent features of country towns and crossroads communities have all but disappeared. With them has gone an able group of tinkers and "fixer-uppers." "Repair" garages have taken over many of the old stands, but for the most part the mechanics are not farm-machinery repairmen. The present-day mechanized farmer in many cases has to be, and in a majority of cases can most profitably be, his own mechanic. A well-equipped shop (which need not be expensively equipped) can be one of the most versatile all-round cost-saving investments on the farm. And on the winter days when there is only barn work to do, then is the time to haul in every piece of equipment that the farmer will be dependent upon at some time during the next year and give it a complete rejuvenation.

When the weather finally breaks in the spring and the soil is just right to turn, that is no time to have to repair the plow. When thunderheads are threatening and the hay is just right to haul is no time for a breakdown. Often many farmers will spend more time "getting ready" to do a job than doing it, simply because getting ready involves some equipment repairs that should have been made the winter before. When that happens, they have slipped up on management.

Some pertinent information on the costs involved in owning and using some of the more common farm tools in one important farming area of the country is presented in the Iowa study by Davidson and Henderson. Figures from their study are given on page 89, not because they may be widely and accurately applied in other areas, but because they provide a good illustration of the relative importance of the different cost items involved in equipment ownership and use and the influence of the amount of use upon the cost per day (which also could have been figured upon an acre or upon an hourly basis).

As essential as equipment is in low-cost farming, it does cost money—during the year when it is purchased and every year thereafter. The farm operator's job is to see that it earns its keep and that he does not become equipment poor and go equipment broke. Proper attention to depreciation is the best constant reminder.

We called at a farm one day where a shiny new tractor had just been delivered. The farmer was as proud as a youngster with a new toy. All the detailed specifications were on his tongue, and he wanted to tell them and to demonstrate the machine. We wondered, while politely reflecting his enthusiasm, whether or not to him that tractor was an end in itself. Was he, after all, seeing it for what it really was—a means to an end, even as his other tools?

Pleasure in fine equipment is understandable and desirable, promising well for the care it will be given. Its function, however, is to save labor, to permit the more timely accomplishment of farm work, and to reduce farm operating costs. It is only a means to that end. Pleasure and pride in ownership should be tempered with the realization that the shiniest new tool starts to depreciate the minute it leaves the dealer's floor.

For the comparative expense value of depreciation, see the table on page 89.

11. Structures Are Production Tools

IT has long been customary to figure the value of a farm at so much per acre with no separate appraisal of fences, wells, service buildings, farm home, or roads. A typical instance is a farm of 118 acres purchased by one of the authors. It had a fairly good seven-room house, two wells, a running stream, six acres of orchard, and the foundation for a large dairy barn, the barn itself having burned down some time before. The local going price for farms was around forty dollars an acre. Slightly less was asked for the farm in question because of the burned-down barn.

Another farm investigated in the same neighborhood comprised 120 acres. It also had an old but fairly well-preserved house.

ANNUAL AND DAILY COST OF FARM MACHINE USE[3]

Machine	Approx. 1941 price	Estimated life, years	ANNUAL COSTS				Annual cost as a per cent of purchase price	Average annual days of use	Cost per day of use
			Depreciation, and interest at 5 per cent	Repairs	Housing, insurance, and taxes	Total			
Tractor plow, 2-14″	$110	17	$ 9.79	$ 3.85	·$2.20	$ 15.84	14.4	16	$1.00
Disc harrow, 10′ single	85	18	7.22	1.28	1.70	10.20	12.0	14	.75
Spike T. harrow, 18′	50	22	3.80	.75	1.00	5.55	11.1	10	.55
Spring T. harrow, 10.5′	55	21	4.35	1.10	1.10	6.55	11.9	7	.95
Grain drill, 10.5′ disc.	210	28	14.05	2.10	4.20	20.35	9.7	5.5	3.70
Corn planter, 2-row	85	21	6.63	1.28	1.70	9.61	11.3	6	1.60
Tr. cultivator, 2-row	120	15	11.50	2.40	2.40	16.30	13.6	17	.95
Mower, 6′ horse dr.	100	21	7.90	3.50	2.00	13.40	13.4	9	1.50
Side delivery rake, 10′	120	21	9.48	1.20	2.40	13.08	10.9	6.5	2.00
Hay loader	135	21	10.65	1.35	2.70	14.70	10.9	8	1.85
Grain binder, 8′ tract. dr.	270	24	19.41	5.40	5.40	30.21	11.2	5	6.05
Corn binder	250	21	19.75	5.00	5.00	29.75	11.9	5	5.95
Combine, 5′	650	11	78.00	16.25	13.00	107.25	16.5	22	4.90
Corn picker, 2-row	750	12	84.00	11.25	15.00	110.25	14.7	14	7.90
Ensilage cutter, 14″	325	18	27.60	6.50	6.50	40.60	12.5	7	5.80
Manure spreader, 70 bu.	170	18	14.45	2.55	3.40	20.40	12.0	28	.75

[3] Davidson and Henderson, *Life, Service, and Cost of Machines on 400 Iowa Farms*, 298.

89

In addition, it had four service buildings of indeterminate function and a huge mow barn. All the service buildings were in very bad repair. A stave silo was leaning perilously, although the staves themselves seemed in good condition. As on the first farm, there were two wells and a running stream. The asking price was slightly over the forty-dollar-per-acre standard.

The first farm was bought instead of the second, not because of a small difference in first cost but because of the buildings. On the first farm, the good foundation suggested that a new barn could be built for a reasonable sum. On the second, the condition of the buildings indicated that not only would there be expenses for repairs, but within a few years, even with repairs, a complete demolition job would be in order, plus rebuilding cost. As it turned out, the man who bought the second farm found that he paid more for rebuilding when it was necessary than his entire original purchase price. The realtor had stressed the point that the salvage in the various buildings probably not only would offset the wrecking charges but also would go far toward furnishing material for rebuilding. This turned out to be a complete misconception. The salvageable material was not worth the cost of the labor to clear away structures that were a fire and wind hazard and that occupied sites obviously desirable for new buildings. In fact, the silo blew down before it could be repaired.

The idea of thinking in price per acre without carefully and judiciously appraising buildings as a separate item is completely fallacious, as many a buyer has found to his sorrow. Another tradition is that the seller should expect to lose on any investment in buildings. In some sections the thought persists that a farm has to change hands two or three times at ever lower sale prices until the value of buildings has been charged off. Thus city buyers are welcomed in some communities because of the belief that the buyer will erect expensive (and sometimes efficient) buildings, then go broke or grow tired of the deal. When that happens, a local farmer can acquire the improvements at a fraction of their original cost.

Obviously, if the only way success can come in farming is to have someone else take losses until capital investment drops drastically below a fair depreciated value, then farming is certainly not a sound industry but a form of junk peddling. Unfortunately, many an itinerant farmer wanders our roads looking for just such junk buys. After a few years on a place, the farmer either finds a "sucker" to buy his present property, or he thinks he sees an even better "junker" and trades or sells himself into the new deal. He usually advantages himself little and certainly makes no contribution to agriculture as a whole.

Since the income tax has applied to farmers, with its allowances for depreciation of service buildings, a clearer sense of the values of these buildings has grown up. The prevalence of obsolete horse barns, of little use once a farm is mechanized, has contributed further to turning farmers' attention to the function and value of buildings.

Farm service buildings have but one use: to facilitate production. If they do not answer this purpose, or cannot be made to do so, they are a detriment rather than an asset. They should provide comfortable quarters for livestock that will promote the most efficient use of feed and encourage economical production, at the same time that they minimize disease. Ton litters of hogs, 10,000-pound cows, and 200-egg hens cannot be expected from cold, damp, dark, disease-ridden structures. What buildings should provide is economical and quality-saving storage for grain, forage, and other farm products—any undue waste or loss of quality is a cost of storage and a profit killer. They should shelter machinery at low cost. If this is their function, the buildings themselves are tools of production, and as such, effectiveness and efficiency in doing their job is as important for them as for power and field machinery.

Service buildings are the United States farmers' biggest item of equipment investment. The 1940 Census of Agriculture shows 28 per cent of the total real-estate and equipment investment of farmers to be in buildings. If we arbitrarily assume that all over the country one-half of this value is in dwellings and one-half in service buildings, then the farm structures that are tools of production had a depreciated value of $16.20 per crop acre in 1940—considerably more than the value of all farm machinery and power.

Yet, unfortunately, many of these structures do not today properly and economically perform the function for which they were intended. A high proportion of major buildings are fifty or more years old. Even if they had been arranged for maximum efficiency when they were built—and many were not—they are today probably out of date. "Unless remodeled, they stand as monuments to obsolete systems of farming. To continue to use them in their present condition is like using a 1920 tractor or a horse-power hay baler."[1]

Striking examples of this failure are to be seen in localities where the type of farming has markedly changed; for example, in former cash hay areas where balloon-sized hay barns were needed to store and cure hay that was later baled for shipment to cities. Now, twenty-five years after other crops have replaced hay, such barns on many farms have been little changed to meet new conditions, and are often more a detriment than an asset. It is not necessary, however, to seek a pronounced change in farming to find outmoded, inefficient buildings.

In the summer of 1942, R. M. Carter of the University of Vermont made observations on twelve Vermont farms of the routines that were followed, the distances traveled, the equipment used, and the time spent in doing dairy chores. He then selected one farm to study in detail with an eye to discovering how much time and travel could be saved if the work routine in the barn were changed.[2] The farm chosen carried a herd of twenty-two cows, and all the work was done by the operator. This fact is highly significant because it reflects high labor accomplishment by this farmer before any alterations were made in his chore methods.

Carter followed the dairyman around the stable with a stop watch and a note pad. He recorded everything that the farmer did, how long it took, and how far he traveled in doing it. The figures were summarized, and the two men put their heads together to see where improvements might be made. The stop-watch performance was repeated at intervals to check progress and determine further steps.

Many small changes were made. Silage, for example, was being fed from a basket, requiring one trip to the silo chute for each cow. A homemade silage cart was substituted, reducing the number of trips from twenty-two to two, saving eleven minutes and 1,870 feet of travel at each feeding. The stable had been cleaned with a wheelbarrow so small that ten trips had to be made to the manure pile.

[1] True D. Morse, "Buildings are Tools," *The Nation's Agriculture,* July, 1945, 7.

[2] R. M. Carter, *Labor Saving Through Farm Job Analysis: 1. Dairy Barn Chores* (Vermont Agricultural Experiment Station Bulletin 503, 1943).

A larger, better-balanced wheelbarrow was constructed, by use of which the stable could be cleaned in three loads, saving 25 per cent in time and 75 per cent in travel. The original routine for bedding the cattle had required eleven and one-half minutes and 1,048 feet of travel; the new routine, seven and one-half minutes and 159 feet of travel.

The stable arrangement was altered somewhat, including a change in stanchion location resulting in two nearly equal rows of cows; a partition was removed around a sawdust bin and silage

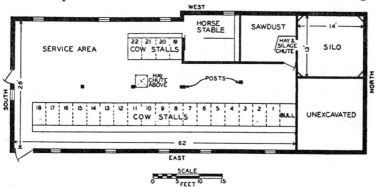

Floor Plan of Stable, Original Layout

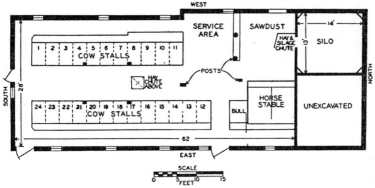

Floor Plan of Stable, Revised Layout

This stable rearrangement made possible a daily saving of two hours on chore time—equal to seventy full days of work saved per year.

With labor at 50 cents an hour and capital at 5 per cent a year a farmer could afford to invest up to $7,000 to save 700 hours of work. The remodeling in this case actually cost less than $100 cash outlay plus work done by the regular farm labor force.

chute, an alley was opened at the end of the stanchion rows to permit circular travel around the stable, and a new door was cut in one wall opposite a cross alley.

The combination of these improvements (see chart), all of which were made over a period of four months without hired labor and with a cash expense of less than $100, made possible a total saving of two hours and five minutes a day in chore time (36 per cent reduction) and of two miles a day of travel within the barn (62 per cent reduction). On an annual basis these savings amount to the equivalent of seventy days' work and 730 miles of walking. Small savings oft repeated certainly add up to big yearly totals and are a challenge to the ingenuity of every farmer. A fifty-pound basket of feed, uselessly carried one hundred feet four times a day, results in thirty-six tons of carrying and twenty-eight miles of walking a year.

In 1944, I. R. Bierly and L. M. Hurd of the Cornell Agricultural Experiment Station asked New York county agricultural agents to suggest some well-organized and well-operated poultry farms on which they might study the routine of poultry chores. They visited eight of the farms and found a variation in the time and travel involved in feeding, watering, and egg gathering per thousand hens ranging from 125 to 670 hours a year, and from 111 to 535 miles of walking a year.[3] The least efficient of the eight poultrymen worked five times as many hours and walked five times as far to care for a thousand hens as did the most efficient.

The reasons for these variations were found to be:

1. The number of birds housed per pen. In large pens, chore work can be done more efficiently because each job is done for a large number of birds at one time.

2. The location of feed rooms in relation to feed hoppers and the method of feeding. Gravity flow of feed directly to or close to the hoppers, large and conveniently located bins that would hold the feed requirements for at least one or two weeks, and hoppers large enough that they did not have to be filled every day were among the labor-saving arrangements.

3. The source of water in relation to the location of waterers

[3] I. R. Bierly and L. M. Hurd, *Steps Take Time in Caring for Hens* (Cornell Mimeographed Bulletin AE 522, 1945).

Multi-row sprayers and dusters are rapidly displacing hand methods wherever market gardening is on the commercial scale. In this Potter County, Pennsylvania, potato field of 240 acres, spraying is done every eight days.

The old hand-dusting method used where labor is cheap. Here in Highlands County, Florida, arsenic and copper lime, a combined fungicide and soil improver, are applied at the same time.

and water disposal. Automatic waterers all year were most efficient.

4. The location of nests in relation to the egg room. Have the hens carry the eggs to the door side of the pen rather than to the far side.

5. The location of roosts in relation to manure chutes. Avoid carrying manure. Let the hens drop it near the disposal outlet.

The results of this study strongly emphasize that a little ingenuity and headwork will save a lot of steps and back work, will make a building more efficiently serve its purpose, and will add to profits.

The number, type, and size of buildings needed on a farm are influenced first by type of farming and second by size of farm. An off-type structure may be very inefficient when not well adapted to the building needs of the particular place. If it is a tool, it has to fit, just as the power and field tools must fit. Justifiable service buildings are those that can be rented profitably to the crop and livestock enterprises. Annual service-building costs run around 10 to 12 per cent of their value.[4] "Unrented" building space is a poor use of funds, in fact a handicap to the owner, just as unrented apartments would be to an apartment-house owner.

Without doubt, building repair and modernization is of concern to many more farmers than is new construction. Numerous "postwar" surveys have shown that extensive building improvement is now planned. If such "improvement" will involve proper modernization to bring building efficiency up to date in relation to the building needs of the farm, probably few other expenditures of funds can contribute more to operating success. Present-day farming with grandfather's buildings imposes too many handicaps on too many farmers.

It is a useful concept that an animal must pay rent for quarters. If building investment is $3.00 a hen, the bird must pay approximately 30 cents rent to cover the annual building costs. It does not necessarily follow that a higher investment with a higher rent would cut profits. Because buildings are tools, building and labor costs should be considered together just as equipment and labor costs should be figured together in crop production.

[4] Paul Williamson, *Twenty-Five Years of Farm Cost Accounts* (Cornell Extension Bulletin 439, 1940), 7.

On an average, about 180 hours of labor are required for the full care and maintenance of one hundred hens for one year. If, in a particularly well-laid-out and convenient structure, the labor could be cut to 150 hours, the thirty-hour saving at 50 cents an hour would be $15.00, or 15 cents a hen. This saving, if all of it is credited to the building, would justify an investment of $4.50 per hen and leave the operator in an equal competitive position with producers using 180 hours of labor in a $3.00-per-bird house.

No, we are not recommending a $4.50 house. We are merely pointing out a principle—figure labor savings and building costs together.

And one more point: Buildings do depreciate. The income-tax laws recognize the fact, and farmers take advantage of that 2 or 3 per cent a year. Mere repairs do not cost that much. A considerable part of the depreciation is in obsolescence. The squirrel rifle is obsolete in war. The ox-team is obsolete in farming. And an 1880 structure is obsolete, likewise, and a profit killer.

In either remodeling or building new, the most modern principle is to get flexibility of design, so that each structure can be readily converted to some use other than its original function if that becomes desirable. Census figures show that the average tenure period for all farm operators is twelve years. The average tenure period of tenant-operated farms (nearly 40 per cent of the whole) is only five years. Yet the life expectancy of most farm buildings is forty years. Thus, most farm buildings have to render service to at least four operators. Because of individual desire and fitness, shifting markets, transportation changes, or any of a number of other reasons, each of these operators may engage in an entirely different type of farming. Obviously, the original builder will help himself most and conserve his own investment to a greater extent if he builds a convertible structure.

Work done at the Iowa Experiment Station indicates that such buildings are entirely feasible.[5] The essence of the idea is that dimensions should be specified to best utilize conventional sizes of materials and recommended pen, stall, or stable footages—which usually figure out in multiples of four feet. Another necessity is to

5 Norval H. Curry and Henry Giese, "Convertible Farm Buildings," *Agricultural Engineering* (Journal of the American Society of Agricultural Engineers), September, 1945.

place pillars and bearing members so as to allow for greatest flexibility of rearrangement.

One new proposal is to construct cheap, more or less unsubstantial buildings. By using relatively inexpensive building boards, plywood, sisalkraft, and similar new materials, structures may be erected for low capital investment. They are not expected to last for much more than a decade, or just about the average tenure of one operator.

Still another plan is to use portable buildings so far as possible. Many of these came into use during wartime. Portable hog houses, brooder and laying houses, cribs, granaries, and other smaller buildings appeared. Conceivably, the owner could move these buildings within the neighborhood from leased farm to leased farm, or to newly purchased land.

The passing (in new construction) of the huge haymow in favor of the separate, one-story hay-storage building indicates farmer acceptance of the theory that such storage cannot be justifiably capitalized under present conditions. Of course, elimination of the fire hazard is also a prime consideration in this plan.

In general, the good manager should analyze his existing structures by asking and answering the following questions:

1. What are my storage losses from rodents, insects, or dampness? Capitalizing the annual loss at 4 per cent will give an idea of what money can be profitably expended for new construction or remodeling.

2. What are my fire hazards? Here a critical examination should be given to possible livestock loss, not just the replacement value of buildings and crops in storage. How about poor wiring, exposed wires, natural flues in the structure, or nearness to an incinerator or other open fire? Abolition of the kerosene or gasoline lantern by electrification under underwriters' rules often is the cheapest insurance that can be bought. Remember that farm fires cost us $100,000,000 a year.

3. How many steps could I eliminate daily if I could rearrange my service buildings any way I wanted to?

4. How much labor could I save if pressure water was installed in my livestock buildings?

5. How much would my milk check be increased if I could

97

raise my grading by cutting bacteria count through more sanitary quarters?

6. How much could I cut chicken mortality if I had proper ventilation, easy sanitation, and less crowding?

7. How many more pigs could I save with proper sanitation, a brooder, self-feeders, and automatic waterers?

8. Could I fire-retard my buildings with new materials and move them closer together to save work and still not increase hazards?

9. Can I afford to let several thousand dollars' worth of machinery rust away when a few hundred dollars will provide housing? (Farm machines do not wear out; they rust out.)

10. Is there any good reason why my chore routine should be the same as grandfather's just because grandfather seemed to get along all right on his production, at prices in his day both for buying and selling? The corollary is: Can I rearrange my buildings to save myself work and provide greater housing capacity that will permit another milker or so, five hundred more chickens, ten more head of feeders, etc.?

The list of questions could be increased indefinitely to cover the individual situation of every farm. It is sufficient to say that if farm buildings were constructed before 1930, more than likely they are not designed for most efficient workability. Even if they were designed since then, there is a good chance that they could be improved in terms of work savings and possible maintenance of quantity and quality of crops in storage. And, even if they were laid out last week, it is possible that improvements can be suggested.

Here is a case where so often the forest hides the trees because of familiarity. We get into habits of work procedure that seem to us to be quite efficient, but an outsider can see at once ways and means to improve the habits. How to get that clear-seeing outsider is the problem.

One way is to write to the National Farm Work Simplification Laboratory, Purdue University, Lafayette, Indiana. From the hints in the literature thus obtained, study your buildings, their internal layout, and their relationship, one to the other, to see if improvement is not only possible but worth while. The difference may turn a red operation into the black.

12. Electrification Is Not a Luxury

IN 1935, only about 10 per cent of all farms were electrified. Eleven years later nearly half had this modern necessity for efficient farming, and a war holding up construction had gone on between the two dates. The plans of both the electrical industry and the Rural Electrification Administration anticipate a near-saturation point of somewhere around 85 per cent by 1955. Thus, electrification may be considered to be out of the controversial stage. Its accomplishment depends upon just how fast the lines can be built. This in part depends upon how quickly co-operatives are formed to petition for REA service, or communities where the potential load will justify the investment prevail upon the private utilities to extend their lines.

Farm electrification has progressed so far that it seems idle now to discuss its pros and cons. Nevertheless, it is true that some farmers say that it is just one more cash-outgo channel, and their whole job in life is to try to curtail or remove such channels. But while a cashless self-sufficiency seems to promise complete security on the soil, it does not provide the standard of living that most of us want.

The cold, hard fact is that the electrified farm has a competitive advantage over the nonelectrified farm that can be met only by the latter's following suit. The following discussion is pertinent here.

THE CHEAPEST HIRED HAND

Electricity has yet to put its best agricultural foot forward. Publicity on rural electrification has stressed the number of miles of strung wire, or the fact that since 1935, when only about 11 per cent of all farmers had "the juice," the percentage has risen to around 50 today. But little attention has been paid to less hopeful facts such as these: only 37 per cent of REA-connected farm homes have pressure water systems, 17 per cent have toilets, 19 per cent tubs and showers; less than a quarter of the farms have small motors; 5 per cent have large motors; only 2 per cent have electric feed grinders.* In short, electricity has been taken to the farm, but

* From a 1944 survey of 11,533 REA members in forty-seven cooperatives, made by *Successful Farming*.

it isn't beginning to do the things it can and should do for the farmer.

No doubt this failure to realize electricity's farm potential comes in part from the farmer's conservative unwillingness to change old ways. A fuller explanation must note that the job of getting poles set and wires strung at the beginning left little time or energy for education of the new farm users. But surely the vendor of electrical supplies and equipment has missed a great merchandising opportunity, while his potential customers have in some cases actually given up hi-line service with a sense of disappointment at the short-circuiting of electricity's high-voltage promises.

An explanation for slow progress in selling farmers on the benefits of full electrification is suggested in a recent article by REA Administrator Claude R. Wickard. Back in 1935 the REA received a letter from a group of utility executives that stated, in part: ". . . there are very few farms requiring electricity for major farm operations that are not now served. Additional rural consumers must be largely those who use electricity for household purposes." In other words, the industry saw future farm electrification as a job almost identical with urban-residence electrification. The utilities did not fully appreciate the manufacturing phases of farming from raw-materials production to partial or complete processing.

In reply, the electrical industry can point out that in 1935 the agricultural depression looked almost permanent. Drought had added to the farmer's woes. The outlook for selling electrical installations was grim. Farmers with low income and ruinous crop prices certainly were not going to be very good prospects for refrigerators, radios, washing machines, and vacuum cleaners—let alone capital goods like electric pumps and feed grinders. Nevertheless farmers in normal times *can* be good prospects if electricity is sold first as a cost-cutting production force and thereafter as a household aid. Traditionally the farmer spends first for his business and second for his family. The new barn precedes the new home.

The mechanics of cost cutting have been plotted in several ways. For example, a farmer hard at work has an hourly personal power output of one-tenth of one horsepower. In a full day (ten hours) he will deliver only as much work as a one-horsepower motor does in one hour. If he buys that labor in manpower, he will pay $4 and up for the day's work. If a motor does the work in an hour, the cost will be less than 4 cents.

This may not seem so impressive if farm work is thought to be mostly field work, for as yet electric motors are not used much in crop production. However, analysts of farm-work routines have shown that on most farms crop production takes fewer hours than crop processing. A widely accepted ratio sets field work at 35 per cent of the farmer's time, barn work at 65 per cent. The rapid spread of field mechanization has greatly reduced crop-production costs, but from the foregoing it is obvious that a still bigger opportunity waits at the barn.

True, the tractor can be backed up to the service buildings to give power to grinders, ensilage choppers, blowers, and similar processing tools, but this is unhandy, takes time, costs more than electricity, and may conflict with jobs that only the tractor can do. The tractor can also pump water—expensively. But small electric motors can do these jobs at low cost and without fuss or temporary neglect of other work. To date, over 225 uses for electrical service on farms have been listed, and new applications constantly appear.

A pressure water system, for instance, is frequently the first electrical installation. The economics of employing this "hired man" have been worked out on an average farm in Ohio in a joint study by Westinghouse and the Ohio Public Service Co. The study showed that when the cows were watered by hand twice a day they produced 216.1 pounds of milk. With continuous water before them, after the pressure system and automatic waterers were installed, they produced 221.6 pounds of milk. The handwork saved came to 175 hours during the five winter months, which at the going hourly wage of 64 cents translated the saving into $112. The milk check increased $36.35 for the extra production—making the total gain $148.35. On the debit side, the cost of juice for the pumping was $1.79. Depreciation on the $282.07 installation at 7 per cent, plus an arbitrary allowance of $5 for maintenance, brought the cost of operation to $26.53. In other words, the system saved $121.82 in its first season.

It might seem that such examples, which exist in variety, would prove conclusively to any farmer who can tap the hi-line that he cannot afford to operate without electricity's savings. However, either the farmer has failed to figure out for himself or he has not been taught that actual cash benefits depend first, on putting the electricity to work, and second, on utilizing the time and labor saved to make more money.

When he understands this, the results can be startling, as brought out by a survey made in 1942 by REA on forty-one electrified farms in Ohio and Indiana. Here are the more significant figures:

	Before electrification	After electrification	Percentage of increase
Acres in farms	7,586	9,630	27
Acres (seed corn)	105	290	176
Milk Cows (number of)	356	520	46
Laying Hens	12,530	19,447	55
Chicks (brooded)	50,025	78,750	57
Chicks (hatched)	350,000	807,000	130
Turkeys	11,000	23,000	109

In order to get a higher return for their labor, the farmers used the time saved by electricity to increase acreage, field crops, and animal units. The story's moral is further emphasized by the fact that the number of full-time men employed dropped from 110 to 103.[1]

The big farmer can purchase and operate ever larger-capacity field machines. But when it comes to efficiency of processing, of buildings and chores done in and around buildings, the little farmer can make electricity give him a fair break, for the advantages of bigness disappear when operations of both sizes are on the rural electric meter. After a minimum consumption which even the smallest electrified farm can meet, there is little saving in mere quantity of wattage consumed. Usually a monthly bill of seven to ten dollars gets the user to the lowest power rate. After that, big farm or little, there is no differential.

Get electricity as soon as you can. Be sure your wiring is ap-

[1] Reprinted from The Farm Column, *Fortune*, July, 1946, 152–54, by courtesy of the publisher of *Fortune*.

proved by the underwriters. Do not save a few pennies on installation economies only to lose dollars in a farm fire. Once the "juice" is on the place, do not try to see how little use you can make of it. Rather, see how much it can save you in livestock losses and in your own labor. Then see how much richness of living it can profit you by lighting your house, lightening the household chores, and providing you with city comforts. More than anything else, it may persuade your children that farming as a way of living is preferable to what the city can offer.

13. Processing Equipment and Vertical Diversification

ONCE, many farm products were processed in whole or part before they left the farm; but with the coming of better transportation and the efficiencies of mass production, the farm became almost entirely a raw-materials producer. Processing was the right of the city. Some students of the farm ills, following World War I, suggested that the only way the farmer could regain his independence was to go back to processing. As they saw it, once again he would make butter for his own use and sale. His wife would wash, card, spin, and weave wool, albeit on a better loom than her grandmother had.

This Thoreau-esque plan enjoyed a certain popularity, especially among city folk. Farmers received the suggestion with notable coolness. During World War II, however, the idea reappeared but with a new twist. It is credited to D. Howard Doane of the famous management service in St. Louis that bears his name.

Mr. Doane reasoned that as long as the farmer stayed in a strictly raw-materials-producer status, he would be continually threatened with the low-wage fate of raw-materials producers the world over. The spread of mechanization and electrification suggested that the farmer could avail himself of power in relatively small packages to do at least the first few steps in processing his products. The farmer need not return to the hand loom, but by himself or in groups, should go ahead to become a small mechanized processor.

Instead of the cotton producer's doing nothing but raising cotton to be shipped north for processing and then returned to the South for sale in shirts, underwear, or sheets, the original producer would do the manufacturing himself. This would retain processing and manufacturing profits within the community. Moreover, it would save transportation of raw material to the mill and finished product back to the consumer in the growing area.

The classic example, however, is soybeans. The heaviest part of soybeans is the cake remaining after the oil is expressed. The cake is used almost entirely on farms as a protein feed supplement. The manner of handling the crop has been to ship the whole bean to a mill, perhaps a thousand miles away. The mill expresses the oil, the lightest part of the product, and ships it usually a short distance to the paint, plastic, or other manufacturer. The heaviest part, the cake, is then shipped back whence it came, for livestock feed. Obviously, most of the cost of the cake is in transportation charges.

Under "Vertical Diversification," as processing-at-home was named by Mr. Doane, neighborhood soybean mills have been set up in dozens of intensive soybean-producing areas. The farmer hauls his beans to the mill, receives a check for the crop, and then, on what used to be a dead-haul, transports the cake back to the farm to feed to his livestock. A scheme of this kind gives the farmer a good price for his raw material, while the cake is cheaper. Obviously, the whole community has benefited, including the owners and operators of the mill that, more often that not, is a co-operative.

This principle undoubtedly will take a larger and larger place in farm life and practice. Freezing lockers and processing plants, canning plants, woodworking plants (to utilize products of farm woodlots), perhaps leather working, and many other raw-material fabricating businesses will spread across rural America. Not only does the plan add value-in-manufacture to the price the raw-materials producer receives, but it also provides opportunities for selling excess farm labor in off seasons.

The idea is new. It is not yet adopted widely. Where it has been tried, it has shown success. Alert managers will investigate and then examine their local situation and crops to find what can be worked out. A whole community may find it expedient to change its traditional cropping plan. There is little doubt that the idea will suggest to certain individuals that they can better themselves by turning their farms primarily into processing plants for the community, with personal farming a side line. Most of all, it is something the individual or community can do without the necessity of going to Washington for federal help.

14. Conclusion

THE first and continuing effort of every good manager in any business is to try to gain as complete control as possible of all the variables that enter into his production picture. Farming, in the past, has lent itself least easily of all industries to gaining this control. Under mechanization, many of the variables can be brought into partial or complete control. The degree that control is achieved is the rating of the manager and a major component of profits.

Practically no business in the world is without risk. Even a theoretical complete control does not rule out the possibility of risk. In farming, near-complete control can be obtained by unlimited investment. It is rare, if not impossible, that buying such control would be profitable when proper charges for interest and depreciation are made. Consequently, the job of the good manager is to calculate just how much increase in production, decrease in costs, and control of variables he can obtain at the justifiable expense.

Too much investment may give increase in production and decrease in operating unit costs, but rental of money and set-asides for replacement may throw the operation into the red. Too little investment may keep interest and depreciation at a minimum, but in the meantime competitors will steal the market on a cost-of-production basis.

Good management not only means adequate tools for kind of crop and size of operation; it also means getting savings or profits by finding greater utilization of tools on and off the farm. If this is not possible, it means utilizing somebody else's tools to the greatest advantage.

In any case, the two major positive considerations in equipment management are: multiplication of human labor in terms of production, and savings in production costs. The two prime negative considerations are the rental charge for money, and the set-aside for replacement (depreciation).

Here is a case history of these principles at work. A few years ago a young man left a promising city job to go back to the farm when his father died. His friends thought his action another sentimental example of the common mistake of a farm boy's continuing the old family homestead even though it obviously offered little opportunity for building up a successful commercial farm business.

Considering the facts at face value, his friends were right. The buildings provided ample space—in fact, more than ample—but were poorly arranged and poorly equipped. The field machinery was of the time-consuming, outdated type. The twenty-five acres of pasture and thirty-five acres of cropland were carrying twelve dairy cows and six heifers, and the dairy was the sole income-producing enterprise. However, time has proved the friends to be wrong. They had reckoned without considering this man's exceptional ability as a manager.

One of his first acts was to cull out the low-producing cows. He put the herd on Dairy Herd Improvement test, continued to weed out unprofitable animals, and got better ones in their place. His father had averaged about 6,000 pounds of milk per cow; within three years after he took over the management, the son was getting 9,500 pounds per cow.

He applied lime and superphosphate to his pastures and meadows and increased his yields of grass and hay. Then, at a cost of $350 plus a good many hours of his own labor, he rearranged his stables, adding seven more stanchions and putting in automatic water buckets. He now carries twenty cows and ten heifers on the same acreage that formerly carried only twelve cows and six heifers.

For a cost of $100, mainly for windows, he converted some little-used barn space into housing for 650 hens. The poultry adds to his volume of business without making additional claim upon his limited land resources; grain is purchased for both poultry and cows.

He is now selling more than two and one-half times as much milk as was sold from the farm under his father's management.

106

Considering both milk and eggs, his volume of produce sold is four times what his father was selling. And, most significant from a net-income point of view, he is doing it with no more labor than his father used. Equipment has taken the place of the extra labor that would otherwise be needed.

At a cost of $550 he had the buildings wired for electricity ($380 for the house, $170 for the barn), and brought in power from the high line a quarter of a mile away. Quite correctly, he looked upon electricity as his cheapest possible "hired man." Its greatest labor-saving uses on this particular farm are for running a milking machine and pumping water for the livestock, each of which has resulted in considerably less chore labor.

The present operator's father milked by hand. His twelve cows had meant an hour and a half of hard work at each end of the day. By machine, the son milks half again as many cows in one-quarter less time.

In rearranging his stables, he provided for driving through the barn from one end to the other with a manure spreader into which the stables could be cleaned with but one handling of the manure—another big labor-saver over the wheelbarrow and wagon his father had used.

In addition to the electric wiring, the milking machine, a new milk house and electric milk cooler, and a manure spreader, the only other important item of equipment that so far has been added to the farm is a buckrake. This tool (mounted on an old car from which the rear part of the body was removed) has made it possible for the operator working alone to pick up hay from the windrow and haul it to the barn more quickly and with much less hard work than by using a wagon.

Except for such assistance as he has from his mother and his sister in caring for the poultry and cleaning the dairy equipment, the man is operating the farm alone. Certainly he is busy. But he is busy at productive work throughout the year, and he works no harder, in terms of the number of hours on the job, than many other farmers who are accomplishing much less production per man. It is most obvious from what he has done that he farms with his head as well as with his hands.

When he went on the farm, he valued the tools and barns at a total of $2,250 on his inventory. The machines he has purchased and the improvements to the barns (including a new milk house and a new wall under the barn) have brought this inventory figure up to $6,150. The farm was previously carrying fifteen animal units of productive livestock, which meant a machinery and barn investment of $150 per unit. It now has thirty-two productive animal units, and a machinery and barn investment of $185 per unit. When this increase in equipment investment is contrasted with the increased production, it is obvious that he has used his equipment well. He had to borrow money to make some of his improvements and additions, but in five years of operation he was out of debt, while he had very nearly doubled the net worth of the farm business.

Much has been said and written about the handicap that large-size, high-speed farm equipment has placed upon the small farm operation, and much of it is true. Here is an example, however, of a type of small farm operation that appears to have met the threat. Some persons might disagree with the conclusions drawn and logically demand more statistics of similar accomplishments. But in many ways a farm business refuses to be a statistic. Hardly any two farms are alike, and hardly any two farmers are alike. The success in this case was built by the man, by his outstandingly able management. The farm he is on would appear to be a handicap to a full expression of his talents, but surely he is not a handicap to it. He illustrates what proper management can do with something less than the best of farm resources with which to work.

PART III: Labor Management

"Your labor is worth what it produces."

15. Your Labor Is Worth What It Produces

"A FARMER is his own boss." If one were to Gallup-poll farmer opinion, no other feature of farming as a livelihood would show up to be so highly prized and so universally cherished. No time clock to punch. No straw-boss to watch him. No one telling him what to do, when to do it, or how. The farmer runs his own show.

Yet, being lord of his domain carries its compensating responsibilities. He must assume every detail of the diverse functions of management; by no means the least important of which is managing himself.

Soil, equipment, and labor are a trinity in farming; the three legs, let us say, upon which satisfactory farm operating results must rest. Management is not a fourth leg. Rather, it is an all-inclusive supporting function which extends across the three—and which jeopardizes the success of the whole venture if any one of the three is not covered or is weak.

The discussion of labor after soil and equipment does not mean that it is third in importance. More logically, it may be said that the reverse is true, at least on the family-operated farms that dominate United States agriculture. A farm provides, first of all, a job for the operator. It is his livelihood as well as his home. In that sense he is the most important factor that goes into the operation, simply because farming, like any other family business, is conducted primarily to make a living.

After the operator's job, the farm may next provide work for other members of the family. Then, only if the family group cannot or does not want to do all the work, is there a place for hired labor. So commonly is the farm thought of as selling produce that the true fact is often overlooked. Actually it is operator and family labor that is being sold. Hired labor is bought for resale. Nevertheless, their own labor is the major resource most farm families have. Their business is operated primarily to furnish them a labor market.

On a dairy farm, labor is sold in the form of milk; on a poultry farm, in the form of eggs and meat birds; on a fruit farm, in the form of apples, oranges, and prunes. As with any other production item, labor's contribution to business success is relative to how much and what quality it produces. In the final analysis, practically everything a farmer does, every management decision he makes, is directed toward selling his own labor and his family labor, if any, to maximum advantage. His main interest is how he can translate his efforts into the greatest possible annual net income.

In brief, a fully employed operator is about the only fixed item that goes into farm operation. Around 3,000 hours of work a year approach the top limit of personal effort that he should or can put into his business. In direct contrast, his land and equipment and his livestock and production supplies may be varied in amount and proportion—and should be so balanced and fitted together as to maximize his production accomplishments.

For two closely related yet distinct reasons, labor and equipment are alternative production items. First, equipment may replace a part of the labor needed on the farm and has replaced labor, because for many jobs farmers have found it to be the cheaper alternative. Second, equipment makes possible a greater accomplishment per man of the labor force that is continued.

Inextricably bound together as these two labor-versus-equipment considerations are, they are still worthy of separate recognition if for no other reason than to emphasize that labor is not eliminated in farming by the purchase of equipment. Equipment expense is justified only so far as it does reduce labor expense or lighten the labor load for the farmer and his family. How well it serves this end is determined primarily by how well the labor and equipment combination on the farm is managed.

Still further, as equipment replaces labor in a farm business, the operator seldom lays himself off. Either hired labor is displaced, or the same labor force is continued and has the capacity to operate a larger business. The net effect of the unending chain of improvement in farm equipment is that the farmer and members of his family take on an ever greater part of the total work. Management of their own labor consequently assumes greater significance in successful farming.

Presumably the operator and his family cannot do the work for which they pay out cash to hired labor. If they could and still hire it done, someone else receives that much of the total returns to labor produced by the farm. That is the intention on farms where the operator does not want the work and his financial position is such that he need not do it. But it is not the intention of able-bodied young farmers who have their farms yet to pay for and their own financial competence yet to build. Their problem is how (within the limits of what they can do) their personal accomplishment may be increased relative to their hired labor and equipment expense.

True enough, wage payments all go to support someone else; they are not lost from the economic system of the country. But that is small consolation to a farmer or a farm family who, because their own labor resources have been used ineffectively, have lost as family labor returns the purchasing power of the wage payments. Plain logic dictates that the first persons to be supported from a farm are the members of the family that operates it. Work effectively and increase the family income is both good economics and good sociology for the individual farm family.

The objective of labor management is commonly expressed as labor efficiency. Many times the first reaction to this statement is: "Oh, you mean work harder. Well, I'm already working as long and as hard as I can, and still ends don't meet." Some farmers work too hard. They have such a forest of work they cannot see the trees that are the individual jobs. They do not manage their work; it manages them. Labor efficiency does not mean to work harder. It means to work more effectively, with greater accomplishment per hour and per year.

Alert farmers are finding ways to make their own labor more effective and cut their hired-labor expense by taking a questioning and challenging attitude toward every job and each part of every job that they do. Sometimes a job can be eliminated; much more often the method of doing it can be changed. Hogs have to be watered, but perhaps the water could be piped to the lot rather than hauled in a tank, with several openings and closings of gates for each trip. Even larger waterers, or larger feeders, requiring less frequent filling might be an improvement.

An inexpensive homemade feed cart might save time out of all proportion to its cost. Perhaps grain could be fed and eggs gathered on the same trip into each pen in the poultry house.

If resulting savings seem to be small, it is worth noting that a saving of five minutes a day counts up to the equivalent of three full days' work in a year. A saving of one minute per cow at each milking in a twenty-cow herd equals a full month of working time (240 hours) in a year.

In the dairy regions of the country, the annual care of one dairy cow requires an average of 150 hours of work.[1] Yet on some farms the feeding, milking, and stable-cleaning chores are so conveniently arranged that only 100 hours per cow are necessary. For a twenty-cow herd the annual difference is 1,000 hours; enough time at average rates of accomplishment to care for 600 laying hens or a flock of 165 ewes, or to raise 16 litters of hogs—entirely with labor saved on the dairy. If the additional livestock is cared for with better-than-average labor efficiency, even these numbers could be increased, possibly to as much as 900 hens, 250 ewes, or 25 litters of hogs.

Obviously, how labor savings should be utilized will depend upon the opportunities presented by the individual farm and upon the interests of the individual farmer. These conditions, of course, are nearly as variable as the number of farms in the country, and entirely preclude any blanket statements about how the time should be employed. Some farmers will place a higher value on it for leisure than for the additional money income that might be obtained by using it productively. Understandable as that decision would be, the fact should not be overlooked that maximum annual income, if that be the operator's objective, is not obtained by part-time work on a farm any more than in a factory. "Logically there should be no unemployment on the farm," says Wilson Gee.[2] But that is a problem that each farmer must face if, by saving time on

1 M. R. Cooper, W. C. Holley, H. W. Hawthorne, and R. S. Washburn, *Labor Requirements for Crops and Livestock* (U.S.D.A. Mimeographed Bulletin F. M. 40, 1943), 130.

2 Wilson Gee, *The Social Economics of Agriculture* (copyright 1932 and 1942 by The Macmillan Company, New York), 141.

one job, he finds it possible to do another, to cut out some hired labor expense, or to sit.

The ingenious and inexpensive devices that some farmers are continually working out to make their labor more effective is a constant challenge to farm-equipment manufacturers and to other farmers alike. Imagination seems to be all one has to have. Some call it laziness. If so, lazy persons are the ones who make the greatest contribution to progress.

A few years ago, a farmer in the Genesee River Valley disassembled the blower fan and stacker pipe from an old grain separator and used it to blow into his barn the straw gathered from behind a combine. His plan worked so well that he tried it for putting in hay, and that worked, too. In 1945, he and his two sons, eleven and fourteen years old, harvested 125 acres of hay (225 tons) without hired help. They used two buckrakes and the blower, and moved hay from windrow to mow at the rate of two and one-half tons an hour—which was more than twice as fast as the traditional hay loader, wagon, and three-man crew. No hand work was involved except shoving hay into the blower.

This same farmer has converted a haymow in one end of his barn into a granary. He has eight square silo-shaped bins that extend up to the plate of the barn. At harvest, his grain crops are combined and spouted directly from the machine into a dump truck. He backs his truck into the barn and dumps it into a receiving bin, from which the grain flows by gravity into a motor-driven fanning mill. After it is cleaned, it spouts down to a catch basin from which a bucket conveyer elevates it to the top of any of the eight bins he chooses to store it in.

Each bin is constructed with a gravity spout at the bottom. If the grain happens to be moist when stored and begins to warm up in the bin, he can spout it out, blow air over it with an electric fan as it flows, even run it through the fanning mill if necessary to cool it down, and elevate it back to the top of the same bin or into another bin without touching it by hand. He can also draw from any combination of bins at one time any desired proportion of different grains, and spout them directly into his feed grinder, with no hand work. He designed the layout himself to fit his own situation and built it at a very nominal cost.

With eight dollars worth of T-iron and his own electric welder, this same farmer built a manure loader to mount on a truck chassis that during hay harvest is used for a buckrake. With it he cleans the heavily tramped manure from his cattle and sheep sheds without hand pitching. Two scoops will fill his spreader.

If this farmer is lazy, more farmers would be more successful if they were lazy in the same way.

Perhaps a farmer should go fishing occasionally, far enough away from his business to think about it objectively—perhaps where he would not catch many fish but could fully relax and think through some problems that he does not have time to consider when the job is panting at his heels. One of the best management services recommends that a farmer should spend ten days a year traveling among neighbors to learn better practices.

For example: Can he make a living wage at certain of the jobs he is now doing? Can he change the jobs or his work methods so that he can better his wage return? Do they contribute enough to the success of the farm business as a whole to justify keeping them, even though the labor returns are small? Do they interfere with more profitable work? Could any of them be replaced with more profitable alternatives? Does he want to replace them—or does he get a compensating satisfaction not measured in terms of money? Yes, there is a place for aesthetics in farming, too, although the whole business cannot very well be operated on that basis.

A new approach to farm-labor efficiency is an adaptation of the technique known as time-and-motion study. It has been used for some time in industrial plants where persons trained in job analysis have been employed to study work routines and develop easier, less time-consuming methods of doing necessary jobs; and at the same time to find ways of eliminating bottlenecks and unnecessary work that interfere with a smooth and rapid flow of material through a plant. The stop watch and the motion picture camera are a part of the tools of their trade used in the study. The analysts break each job down into minor parts in order to analyze it in detail, the theory being that many tiny savings oft repeated bulk to imposing totals. An instance has come to our attention where six highly paid production men in a large manufacturing plant worked together for a full day on the problem of reducing the manufacturing cost of one small part that went into their product. All they accomplished was to cut the cost one-half cent— a wholly insignificant saving when only one unit is considered; but the plant makes ten million of these parts a year, on which the saving totaled the by no means insignificant sum of $50,000.

Significant as the results of studies of this nature have been in industry, the method has been little used in farming. Farm work has not generally been considered adaptable to stop-watch analysis. Yet much of it is; Carter's study (see page 92) is a case in point that could be repeated many times over from other studies made under the pressure of wartime labor shortages.

In December, 1942, with the farm-labor situation becoming increasingly serious, Dan M. Braum, of the United States Department of Agriculture, appeared before a Senate subcommittee and testified on the importance of job-analysis studies in agriculture to help meet the farm-labor problem. "An example [of what might be accomplished] . . . ," he said, "is the work of Marvin Mundel, an industrial engineer at Purdue University. Marvin Mundel was called by a hatcheryman to help him on the principles of work simplification. They worked together for one-half day and made motion pictures, and analyzed the job of sorting baby chicks. . . . As a result of that half-day's work they saved 40 per cent in time and did a better job, with no added equipment."[3]

An appropriation by the General Education Board of the Rockefeller Foundation made possible the inauguration of farm-work simplification studies on a national basis at the beginning of 1943. Headquarters were established at Purdue University under the direction of E. C. Young and L. S. Hardin. Co-operative studies have been conducted at twelve land-grant colleges from Florida and New England to Washington and Oregon. Many persons believe that the results of these investigations may eventually be considered the most important developments in modern farm management. Maximum emphasis has been laid upon labor saving in relation to the war emergency, but the principles established and the techniques developed may well provide the margin for many farms between staying in business and going bankrupt in the critical years ahead.

[3] *Technological Mobilization:* Hearings before a Subcommittee of the Committee on Military Affairs, U. S. Senate, 77 Cong., 2 sess., on S. 2721 (December, 1942), 747.

The list of farm jobs that have been studied is highly diverse, including dairy cattle, feeder cattle, hog and poultry chores; the removal of brush from orchards; the harvesting of feed crops, truck crops, sugar beets, and tobacco; cutting seed potatoes; and so on. The General Education Board has withdrawn from the picture as of mid-1945, but the work will continue at the agricultural experiment stations.

Fresh and pertinent as this point of view on farm-labor efficiency may be and valuable as the results of these studies are, they are of no use to the farmer who does not adapt them to his own farm. Even worse, they may show the way for others to gain a vital competitive advantage if they put them to use and he does not.[4]

"Among the materials you have to work with and manage is time," says E. C. Young.[5] "You have as much time to work with as any other farmer—no more, no less. How you use it affects your results. Planning your use of time is of the very essence of good farm management. A good farmer knows, tonight, what he is going to do tomorrow and the day after, as well as next week. He knows, too, what he is going to do if it rains. You can explain many of the differences in results obtained by successful and unsuccessful farmers by their differences in day-to-day work planning, thinking ahead, getting everything ready beforehand. Success with crops and livestock depends to a very great extent on doing things right, at the right time, in the right way. The man who has planned his work and is ready to cultivate when the soil is in the most favorable condition, and when weeds are at just the right stage for destruction, not only stands a good chance of getting a bigger crop than his planless neighbor, but also is likely to get it with less work."

You and your family have all your labor to sell. How well you may live depends upon how successfully you sell it in the competitive game of commercial farming. That is the pay-off on labor management, and it is measured in the quantity of product you have left for your labor after other production costs are paid.

[4] A list of publications reporting on farm-work-simplification studies may be obtained from the Director of Information, Bureau of Agricultural Economics, Washington, D. C.; from E. C. Young or L. S. Hardin, Purdue University, East LaFayette, Indiana; or from state agricultural experiment stations.

[5] *Farm Engineering and Management: Assignment Four* (Washington, National Youth Foundation, 1940), quoted in the *Journal of Farm Economics*, February, 1944, 238.

The principles of labor management apply equally to your labor as the farm operator, to your son's labor, and to your hired labor. The more effectively the family labor supply may be used (not, let us repeat, in terms of harder work but of more efficient work), the less hired labor will be necessary to run the farm. It is kindergarten simple that the less hired labor to be paid from a given volume of production, the greater will be the returns for labor to you and your family.

16. Jobs for Sale—Cheap

SUCCESSFUL farming should pay interest on the money invested plus the going rate of wages for labor and management. Some farms meet this test of success. Many more do not.

Common practice is for a farmer to figure his net income as the difference between gross receipts and operating expenses. More often than not this works out to be less than he could get if he were to sell his labor in a factory. Even then the sum does not all represent labor income. A part is the earnings of his capital. If all farmers were to deduct hourly wages for themselves at the prevailing rate for hired help, a majority would have nothing to enter on that line in the account book marked "interest on investment." Or, if interest were deducted first, the remaining wage too commonly would be a pittance.

A farmer invests money in a farm primarily to buy a job. The quality of that job sets the effective ceiling on his living standards. Study after study from all parts of the nation has shown close correlation between the size of the farm and the value of the job the operator holds. Size of farm does not necessarily mean number of acres, although we have fallen into endless misconceptions, enacted many poor laws, and set up useless rules and systems of advice on the erroneous basis of acreage.

A quick review of Part I will show many reasons why a judgment of size on an acreage basis is wrong. Ten acres of one soil type may be as productive as 100 acres of another type. Sixty-five acres of land may make a good living for one family in New Jersey, while 120 may be necessary in Wisconsin. An 80 may do well in famed Lancaster County (Pennsylvania), while that amount of land in

Valencia County (New Mexico) will provide a living for only two or three head of beef cattle. The 160 which the drafters of the Homestead Act thought right for the High Plains proved to be one of the worst bobbles in agricultural history. On the other hand, a half-dozen acres of California citrus have made much more than a good living for many operators.

Even a dollar description of size does not fill the bill. A man might starve to death on $5,000 of truck land close to a big city, yet get along quite well on the same amount spent for a diversified farm in certain parts of Oklahoma. A recent survey in Indiana showed that to "buy" as much income as his hired man gets, an owner must be prepared to make an investment of $17,000.

Farm sizes have come about in almost every way except the rational. In older sections of the country, topography had a lot to do with size. Where mountains, streams, outcroppings of rock, or existence of swamps made natural boundaries, farms were laid out "as Nature intended." Unfortunately, Nature has little truck with bookkeeping.

Many farms that were once full family size (under a horse economy) have been divided again and again to be parceled out to sons and daughters at estate settlements. Today they are too small to provide full-time employment for a single worker. Still elsewhere, and the situation is growing more common, farms may offer a full year of employment under horse operation but definitely do not under modern power machines. This latter circumstance is probably the greatest single factor in the steady shift toward larger farm acreages as shown by the Census.

Here let us insert a word of caution on quick acceptance of the seeming import of those Census figures. True, the "average" farm—which does not exist but is simply a statistical abstraction—shows more acres today than in 1930. There are more farms of larger size than there were a decade ago, but also there are more smaller farms. Farms of intermediate acreage are losing out to these divergent trends.

It is untrue to say that none but the big-acreage farmer can exist in our modern farm economy. It is likewise untrue to say that all farms soon will be very big or very small, and that the latter will be only part-time or subsistence farms.

Actually, there is a tendency under good conservation practices to throw more and more land that should never have been plowed into pasture or rangeland. There is a corollary tendency to throw one-time "ten-acres-and-a-mule" cotton farms into large combinations for livestock operation. Similarly, a managed grassland program of the Northeast and North Central states (just getting underway) tends to combine uneconomical units, taking them out of row-crop production and putting them into managed forage and pasture. Again, a growing number of range operators at last recognize that ranges have long been overstocked; hence they are buying small ranches and consolidating them into bigger units where opportunity permits. All these factors make dramatic changes in "average" farm size.

Against this movement, there is a healthy growth in small, intensively farmed tracts for truck crops and specialty farming. Modern poultry husbandry does not require much acreage, but it does require much capital. A successful broiler factory may occupy only a few lots near a concentrated market. Cut flowers are another small-acreage user, although the annual income may run into figures which sound like a plantation operation. And as more and more new machines, designed for small acreages intensively operated, appear on the market, undoubtedly more people will find appeal in this type of farming.

If ever we saw two persons who could turn a lot of produce from a small acreage, they are a little, stooped English gardener and his wife, who at middle age emigrated to Canada and thence to the United States. They farm ten acres close to a northern city and sell poultry, garden truck, herbs, flowers, and plants at the Farmer's Market. Every bit of that ten acres looks as a garden is supposed to look when it is being planned from a seed catalog on a winter evening.

The wife cares for the chickens and the flowers, helps to prepare the load for market, and in busy times may do the selling. At other times, both husband and wife go to market Tuesday, Thursday, and Saturday of each week, and there take as much pleasure in selling to regular customers as they do in growing and preparing the products to sell. Their season begins with the earliest of vegetables and with plants raised under glass. Succession plantings carry through the summer and fall. Radishes may grow between rows of peas and come off before they are crowded for room. Beans or some other of the twenty-five or thirty vegetables they raise may be planted shortly before the peas are harvested and come on to occupy the land as soon as the pea vines are removed. Endive or some other late crop follows a midsummer harvest of another vegetable. All summer the dooryard and various odd corners riot in bloom, and the flowers turn into dollars.

A storage cellar prolongs the season, but when the holidays come, everything is cleaned up, the chickens accompany the last of the garden produce to market, and the good people vacation in Toronto.

They are a talented team in their production efforts, each complementing the other. They operate a successful farm, as their comfortable home and living attest. Their acreage does not measure the size of their business—it is the amount of produce they raise and sell. Perhaps they do not realize that themselves. "I've worked for others all my life until we came here," the husband said. "Here we have our own place," and pride in that fact showed in his face. "We're busy, but we like this farm. Any family that can't make a good living from ten acres or even less just aren't good farmers."

The fact that not everyone wants to operate a truck farm and make an important part of his total return by selling at retail, and, more important, that not all farmers could if they wanted to, are points he chose to overlook. Ten acres are enough for him, as they would be for other equally skilled producers in the same type of farming. The couple has the proper farm size (for them) because that size is adequate to provide all the employment they want at a wage return that is satisfactory. In short, they bought the kind of jobs they wanted.

Let us insert here, parenthetically, that not all farmers are unhappy, or consider themselves a problem, or are overly desirous of changing their jobs, their farms, or themselves. A contented man makes few headlines. When farm leaders, legislators, and soap-box orators tell the public that they "speak for all farmers," or represent all farmers, and that all farmers are complaining about something or a number of things, either the speakers are ignorant or they are willfully ignoring the facts. Actually, as in the example above, there are a great many people who have bought themselves satisfactory jobs and are living rich, full lives. Some are small truck and poultry farmers. Some are Iowa tenant farmers and would not be owners when they could. Some are live-at-home farmers down in Arkansas. And not a few are contented little ranchers in the cattle country, where popular belief has it that only a "big rancher" can conceivably be happy.

One of the most contented men we have ever known runs a brood herd of only forty cows on a section of land he homesteaded in Catron County, New Mexico. His total net worth at peacetime prices would not be more than a few thousand dollars. Most of his food comes from cans, pieced out by trout which throng the streams on and near his place, wild turkeys which are abundant, venison, rabbit, quail, and pheasant. Obtaining the latter food items provides his recreation as well as part of his living. The sale of his spring calves and game-animal skins gives him enough cash to operate his secondhand automobile, replace it with another every five years, go to an occasional movie, buy whatever interests him in the mail order catalog, and—what is very important to him —read books like this. He explains that studying in books about how much trouble the other fellow has to make a living keeps him contented with his lot.

What keeps the world aware of the "farm problem" and the troubles of farmers is the discontent of so many of them. Part of that discontent is the healthy ambition of individuals who want to better themselves or provide better advantages for their children than they enjoyed themselves. Part is the unhealthy discontent of the misfit, the man who has no place in farming, the individual who thinks the world owes him a living, and that new class who believe that the government should support everybody in whatever kind of life he elects. For the latter we can offer nothing here.

For the person who is willing to study, analyze his own position, and accept the proposition that there are ways of changing the horizons of his farm job other than merely asking for ever higher prices for farm products, here is an invitation to read further. If your present operation is not paying off at least to the extent of a good wage (providing your soils are fertile and your equipment adequate), then unhesitatingly we recommend critical consideration of the size of your business. This dogmatic statement is made only because the outstanding common reason for poor success on American farms is that the operation is not large enough to provide a full work year.

It costs on the average $8,000 to provide the tools and housing to make one job in the automobile industry. The industry could not afford to invest this amount of money if it operated only part of a year. Yet, on farms we often invest much less per worker than industry does, then operate at only a six months' capacity and still expect a decent wage. We hasten to admit that investment per man in industry does not necessarily have direct bearing on investment per man in agriculture; but the farm orator commonly tells his farmer listeners that they deserve public assistance because "they work from dawn to dusk for only a fraction of what the industrial worker receives."

Maybe the farmer does work from dawn to dusk, but in most cases for only part of the year. Again, he may work from dawn to dusk for the full year, but his output per man-hour is much lower than that of his colleague in the factory. That output may be cut down by too small investment. It may be reduced because his work techniques are so much less efficient than those of the factory workers. In most cases, it is a combination of both. Even given efficient output per hour, total output may be limited by size of operation.

Consequently, let us examine the various classes of American farms in terms of labor employment. We will start with the largest group in number, that is "the too-small farm." Remember, we are not speaking of acreage now, but of a farm unit, no matter what its acreage, which cannot offer full, effective employment. Then let us proceed to "family-type farms," "family-commercial farms," and finally, "big-business farms."

The Farm Census of 1945 (last count of farms available at this writing) reported a United States total of 5,900,000 properties called farms. To a great majority of people the word "farm" calls to mind one particular property with which they are familiar—or possibly the sort of farms that are common in their own part of the country. When applied to six million units spread over forty-eight states, it has no definite meaning. It covers one-mule cropper units and many-mule plantations; highly productive corn and livestock farms in the Middle Western heartland; wheat, cattle, sheep, and a variety of specialty farms (ranches) in the West; fruit farms, vegetable farms, dairy farms, and poultry farms scattered widely over the country; some of which, in each case, are larger than average, others smaller than average—and "average" means nothing at all. Yet each "farm" is both home and job to an operator, and may also be to family workers and hired workers. Each one that is a commercial operating unit presents problems of organization and management that differ (but only in degree) from the problems presented by others; but the problem common to all is a living for the operating family. It is the final objective of management, and it is accomplished from production.

The reason most farmers are inadequately employed is that the most common type of farm, although it may contain few or many acres, is too small in the employment opportunity it provides. Specifically, *a small farm is one that does not provide an adequate market for the labor of one able-bodied man, using reasonably up-to-date equipment and work methods for the type of farming being done.*

Of the over six million farm units reported by the Census of 1940, the Bureau of the Census and the Bureau of Agricultural Economics in joint study have classified one and one-quarter million as merely nominal farms.[1] If these properties should be called farms at all, they are very small farms indeed, in the sense of the farm-employment opportunity they afford. Many are rural residences and retirement homesteads on which there is little intention of commercial farming, since they had neither horse nor tractor power and raised less than $750 worth of produce (an average of only $250 worth). To call them farms merely because they fit the very broad Census definition of a farm is confusing the issue. Excluding them from consideration among farms leaves 4,857,000 farm units in 1940, not the 6,097,000 commonly referred to because the Census reported that many.

In addition, the Census-BAE study classified 3,182,000 other farm units as "inadequate" to support properly a farm family. This number alone is 52 per cent of all farms reported by the 1940 Census, a surprisingly large proportion. These farms average 1.4 workers each, but produced only $491 worth of produce in 1939.

1 Bureau of the Census and Bureau of Agricultural Economics, co-operating, "Analysis of Specified Farm Characteristics for Farms Classified by Total Value of Product," summarized and discussed by John M. Brewster in "Farm Technological Advance and Total Population Growth," *Journal of Farm Economics,* August, 1945, 516–18.

On the basis of number of workers employed, these so-called "inadequate" units appear to be excluded from the category of small farms as defined above. However, there are many farms on which one man or even more workers keep busy that would not provide full employment for one man if they were properly equipped and work methods were effectively planned. Most of the units included in this 52 per cent appear to be exactly in that position, because in 1939 their production per man was less than half as great as that on the farms that were termed "adequate" family units.

If these figures may be accepted as accurate, and they are the best available on size differences in United States farms, then 75.2 per cent of the farms in the country (1940 count) are "too-small farms" by the definition given.

Some of these many units have never been anything but country homes on which the families' intentions are primarily to have a place of residence rather than a commercial operation. Others are ten-acres-and-a-mule cropper units. Still others are farms that may have been adequate at one time, but for one reason or another have been by-passed in the development of modern agriculture. In any rural community in the older parts of the country, there are large numbers of farms "that supported and educated a family of ten when Grandfather Brown was farming it," but today provide a very meager living for much smaller families.

Many of them are still "grandfather farms" in the sense that they are still operated much as grandfather operated them, with grandfather's equipment and grandfather's work methods. And their down-at-the-heel appearance shows their lot to be a hard one among present competition. Poor soil, poor soil management, inability to raise capital for equipment and improvement, or poor business management—any one or a combination of these factors may have contributed to the decline. With the low cash costs of farming and living in grandfather's day, grandfather may have had money for paint where now there is not money for shingles.

Small farms need not all be unsuccessful, as has been shown; but as many are being operated, they fail to produce a "fair" return if, indeed, any return at all for the work done on them. On the average, they are the least well equipped, the least up to date of any United States farm-size group.

The family farm, epitomizing the Jeffersonian ideal of agriculture, comes next above the small farm in size range. Yet the whole idea of a family farm is something of an anomaly. It has been called variously the family-size farm and the family-type farm. The concept of "family size" is exceedingly indefinite and therefore of little usefulness. This becomes apparent when it is recognized that a "family" is a variable, and thus one variable, a farm, is being defined in terms of another variable, a family. Small wonder that the idea of "family size" has caused confusion.

A "family-type" farm, which by contrast denotes in broad terms only an operating relationship between land and people, seems much to be preferred. The family-type farm, depending upon one's definition, may be a subsistence unit on which the intentions are to produce primarily for home consumption, or a commercial unit operated with the intention of raising products to sell. Many family-type subsistence units are included in the inadequate farms listed above. Subsistence farming provides a Henry David Thoreau, if not, indeed, a Robinson Crusoe existence, in which management is a comparatively minor matter.

The term "family-commercial" farm has been suggested.[2] It seems to fit admirably our purposes for denoting all that middle-sized group of farms between small farms, as defined above, and big-business farms. With the hope that it does not add chaos to confusion, we define a family-commercial farm as: *A farm that provides as a minimum an adequate market for the labor of one able-bodied man, and as a maximum an adequate market for the labor of an operator and his family, plus any number of hired hands that enable the family to sell its own labor to better advantage.*

Certainly that definition is very broad, but there seems to be no other logical limitation on the upper side except that the operator and family members shall remain a part of the labor force. Debate concerning where the upper size limit should be is more academic than practical, but it appears to lie somewhere in that indefinite range where the operating emphasis shifts from the net returns for operator and family labor to a primary interest in the

[2] M. R. Benedict, F. F. Elliott, H. R. Tolley, and Conrad Taeuber, "Need for a New Classification of Farms," *Journal of Farm Economics*, October, 1944, 694–708.

return on invested capital. At the point in size where the operator ceases to be one of the laborers on the farm, the problem of labor management tends to change also.

If the family-commercial type of farm is the ideal in United States agriculture (to some it is, and to some it is not), then it appears to have failed to make the grade. At least, it is not so dominant in rural America as is commonly believed. If 72.5 per cent of farm units are small farms, a maximum of 27.5 per cent could be family commercial. Perhaps it is just a matter of definition, and one could count a large number by using a different definition. But, with no intention of being facetious, we could also count more horses in the country if the definition of a horse were broad enough to include cows.

"Adequate" family units to the number of 1,584,000, or 26 per cent of the total in 1940, were reported by the Census-BAE study. What is called "adequate" is probably in fairly close agreement with the family-commercial definition given here, since the farms included in this one and one-half million averaged 2.2 workers each.

Another 91,000, or 1.5 per cent of United States farms in 1940 were classed as large-scale units. These are farms considered by the Census-BAE personnel to be beyond the family-farm size. They counted as such the farms that had a value of product of $10,000 or more in 1939, or that were valued at $40,000 or more. They are included here because of the startling fact that they account for nearly 20 per cent of total farm production.

Very probably some farms that were counted as large-scale units would meet the broad definition given for a family-commercial farm. In any event, the number of large-scale farms in the United States is small, although their production effect is out of all proportion to their numbers. To complete the series of definitions, this is offered for a large-scale farm: *A farm that is beyond the size of providing a labor market for a farm family, on which all labor is hired, and on which the primary operating objective is a return on capital investment.*

"The principal characteristic of these farms that differentiates them from the farms in the family-commercial group is the amount of labor employed and the method of handling it. Their relations

The two-row peanut harvester developed by U.S.D.A. engineers digs, shakes, and windrows the vines ready for stacking and curing, thus cutting costs materially under traditional hand methods.

Tractor-drawn potato digger at work at Presque Isle, Maine, is already obsolete as new complete harvesters are announced for early manufacture.

with labor follow more closely the pattern prevailing in industrial plants than those characteristic of the family farm. Both they and their workers are confronted with special problems of recruitment, housing, wage determination, and other related problems."[3]

Units such as these do not dominate United States agriculture, as it has sometimes rather loosely been stated. Nor is it to be expected that they will, as will be discussed later. It is significant with regard to the food base of the country that "adequate" family units and the large-scale farms, together comprising 27.5 per cent of all properties listed as farms in 1940, accounted for nearly 70 per cent of United States farm production, and nearly 80 per cent of the farm products marketed. Thus, it is not so much six million farms employing ten million workers that is the farm foundation of the United States industrial structure as it is one and three-quarter to two million farms employing four to four and one-half million workers. And it is this smaller number of farms that dominate the market provided by 115,000,000 nonfarm consumers.

These are the farms that set the pace to which the small farm must adjust, if the labor market that the small farm provides is to return a "fair" wage for the work done. Furthermore, the most efficient producing units within the adequate and large-scale groups are the pace-setters for all other farms. The trend is toward ever more efficient operation; some farms lead, less successful farms follow.

We hold that on all commercial farms, except the large-scale units, the prime criterion of success is the net returns to operator and family labor. Yet, since hired labor is bought to be resold, with the intention and expectation of profit, a sweeping principle seems justified. It makes no difference what size of farm one operates, or where it fits in to the small-farm, family-farm, or big-business-farm classification, for basic to successful operation is the accomplishment of the labor force as expressed by production per worker. Only in details and in degree do management problems change with size of farm; the principles remain the same.

Thus, on any given farm unit there is a certain optimum ceiling for effective labor employment. Below that optimum the wage rate per hour or per year will be reduced. This was the commonest

[3] Benedict, Elliott, Tolley, and Taeuber, "Need for a New Classification of Farms," *Journal of Farm Economics*, October, 1944, 694–708.

situation before the war, as is shown by the fact that production rose nearly a third during the war years with five million less people employed on farms. Even discounting the unusually fine weather, it is still obvious that farming was not giving optimum employment before the war under the conditions then existing.

There is little doubt that during the war on some farms the labor expended went beyond the optimum, for purely patriotic reasons. That is, on some Corn Belt farms eighty acres of corn to one man may have provided optimum labor return, yet because of the emergency many farmers handled one hundred or more acres. The extra effort may have been paid for in ill health, fast depreciation of machinery, and expensive replacement of fertility reserves.

In peacetime, without the mitigating factor of patriotism, it is an unwise operator who continues his input of labor beyond the optimum. As an example, let us suppose that a one-man dairy operation, by employing machines and modern techniques, has raised the productive unit to twenty cows. Assume that the operator is fully employed at that point and has an optimum hourly labor return. By adding a few cows to the herd, he may increase his gross return; but because of added feed purchases, more personal work (beyond what he can reasonably do), or hired labor expense, his own labor return might be reduced. In that case, he has passed an optimum point and should stop to take stock.

Analysis may show that to increase his net income—not his gross—he needs more land, more or better buildings, more machines, or a considerably larger herd and a hired man.

Too many farms operate either with 1.2 or 1.7 men on what is really a one-man unit operation, or else they are employing two men for a 1.2 or 1.7 operation. In either case, management is unsuccessful for underemployment (or conceivably there can be overemployment) is cutting net hourly returns. Full effective employment being the desideratum, the changes indicated are to adjust the size of business.

In general, progress in mechanization and techniques and the achievement of better seed strains indicate that a change is desirable to increase production to better utilize the labor available. However, in special cases, the new factor of surpluses may mean the preferable change to be toward lower production while still maintaining full employment for fewer workers.

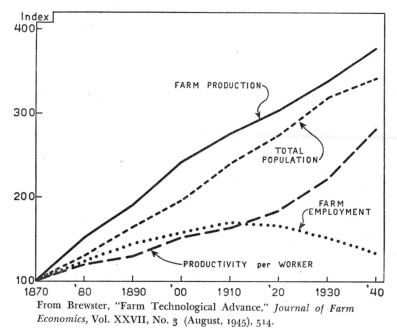

From Brewster, "Farm Technological Advance," *Journal of Farm
Economics,* Vol. XXVII, No. 3 (August, 1945), 514.

*Farm Production, Farm Employment, Farm Labor Productivity,
and Total Population*
United States, 1870–1940 (Index numbers, 1870=100)

A greater increase in the productivity of farm workers than in the
total population of the country is squeezing an increasing number
of farmers off the land.

In any case, do not expect a part-time farm to give full-time
wage rates by appeal to Washington for more farm legislation.
The taxpayers are nearing revolt, and farmers today form the
smallest portion of the tax-paying public in the entire life of the
nation.

17. How Big a Job Can a Small Farm Offer?

LABOR productivity that was good enough to meet the competition a generation ago is not good enough today. That, in
the final analysis, is what is the trouble on "grandfather farms."

They are operating units that could pay the going rates of wages in grandfather's time and provide a good living for his family according to the standards of his day. Now, however, they do not return a fair wage for either family or hired labor, simply because they have not, for one reason or another, kept abreast of the developments in farming that have made possible an increase in labor productivity.

At the time of the Civil War, three pecks of wheat would hire a harvest hand for a sunup-to-sundown day in the fields. The wheat cost of labor has steadily risen to reach two and one-half bushels a day in the decade 1935–44.[1] Many farmers will say and are saying that two and one-half bushels of wheat a day represent high wages. They do. But in truth a farmer is not fighting against high wages per se. He is fighting against rates of labor productivity that are higher than his own. Wage rates are only an expression of productivity, and the current wage rate reflects, to a high degree, the average level of productivity. A hired man provided with tools and working conditions which allow him to produce more than he costs is working for the farmer. If he produces less than he costs, the farmer is working for the hired man.

Nor is this principle important only where hired labor is involved. The farmer, to make the equivalent of hired man's wages, must accomplish equivalent production himself. That point brings up the one significant modification that should be made of emphasis on production per man: On small farms, the total volume of production may be of first importance—not that accomplishment per man is any less vital than on large farms, but the limiting factor may be enough total production to justify the full time of one man.

For example, one man with the proper equipment and well-laid-out work routine can care for twenty dairy cows and produce the forage crops to feed them. How, then, can a farm with a total business equivalent to ten or twelve cows provide fully productive

1 Calculated from data published by the United States Department of Agriculture. See also T. E. LaMont, *Agricultural Production in New York, 1866–1940* (Cornell Experiment Station Bulletin 769, 1941); Harold Barger and Hans H. Landsberg, *American Agriculture, 1899–1939: A Study of Output, Employment, and Productivity* (New York, National Bureau of Economic Research, Inc., 1942); and John M. Brewster, "Farm Technological Advance and Total Population Growth," *Journal of Farm Economics*, August, 1945, 516–18.

employment for one man? This question is pertinent for inadequate farms that want to be profitable commercial units.

Only in part is the problem one of labor management. As a starting point, the fully productive use of labor implies adequate, up-to-date, and properly used equipment. And then the labor-equipment combination must be used on large enough units of productive land and efficient livestock for the labor not only to be kept busy but to turn out the produce that is the first objective.

R. E. L. Greene of the North Carolina State College of Agriculture has well summarized the point.[2] While his comments are applied to his own state, they are no less pertinent elsewhere. He says: "A farm to be successful should give the operator and his family a relatively full-time job. My observations in North Carolina are that too often the so-called 'family farm' does not utilize more than half of the available labor. Such farmers need to do 50 to 100 per cent more business than is being done to begin to utilize their resources efficiently.

"From the standpoint of efficient production, the size of the farm should be large enough to accomplish the following objectives:

"1. To furnish the farmer and his family relatively full employment throughout the year.

"2. To enable the operator to make effective use of the modern farm equipment adapted to his operation.

"3. To enable the operator to employ modern farming practices.

"Prosperous agriculture can be based only on economic farm units that make the attainment of these objectives possible. It is not possible to raise the level of living of a large part of the farm population so long as they have to obtain their income from small business units that are basically inefficient producers."

Obviously, adjustments such as Dr. Greene's statement suggests cannot be made on every farm that is of inadequate size. The additional capital investment for equipment, livestock, and production supplies is out of the question for some families, except through a public program of rural relief. And some, because of poor land resources, could not profitably use these aids to produc-

[2] In correspondence with the authors.

tion if they had them. They are the families on the hopeless kind of farmlands that J. Russell Smith has so aptly called "Land of Do Without."

Still further, if two or three million farm operators were to make these adjustments, there would not be enough good land in the country to go around and fewer farms could be maintained. John M. Brewster points out that: "Were the national farm plant organized so as to enable families on 3,182,000 inadequate units to be as productive as those on average adequate units, these smaller farms might be replaced by approximately 1,000,000 units. Assuming that each unit represents five persons, this reorganization would call for approximately a 35 per cent decline in the 1940 farm population."[3] (According to preliminary figures of the 1945 farm census, there was approximately a 20 per cent decline in five years, yet production was up well over 30 per cent.)

United States agriculture has been overcrowded—a condition brought about by an average increase in the productive efficiency of farm labor that has been greater than the increase in the buying power of the national population, or of the national population plus export outlets. Only in the recent war period, and for a short period of reconstruction, was the situation reversed. Yet in spite of the wartime demand for farm products, the farm population of the United States declined. A more rapid increase in the average productivity of farm workers than in the total population of the country, particularly since 1920 (see chart on page 129), is squeezing an increasing number of farmers off the land. The least competent managers, those who cannot or do not meet the trend in production per man, are squeezed out first, or accept a substandard level of living if they remain in farming.

On the other hand, "there is not one farm problem but 6,000,-

[3] "Farm Technological Advance," *Journal of Farm Economics*, August, 1945, 516–18. Brewster footnotes this statement with the following remarks: "While the present discussion is in terms of actual farms, it is recognized that nominal farms (or whatever else one may call them) are of great social importance and may become increasingly so because agriculture offers some opportunities for persons who on account of age, incapacities, or handicaps of any kind, can contribute to their self-support." With this statement we agree in full. Like Brewster, however, we are concerned with commercial farming, since it is in commercial farming that the problems of management are of major concern.

ooo of them."[4] Whatever the broad problems within the agricultural industry as such, and whatever the solutions may be, any one farmer is concerned primarily with his own competitive position. The trends outlined above serve only to indicate how extremely competitive United States commercial agriculture has become; and although the basic principles of business management have been taught for years, by no means are all business units successfully managed. On the good and sound basis of history, no one farmer need worry, if he keeps abreast of progress, about what the increased efficiency of another will do to him. He must seize every opportunity, just as the neighborhood grocer must if he is to meet the competition of the chains.

Improved technology in agriculture—whether better equipment, improved seed and livestock, better fertilizers and soil-maintenance practices, better disease and pest control, or better work methods as determined by work-simplification study—is the very essence of increased labor productivity on farms. On frequent occasions statements have been made that such improvements tend, in the long run, to be to the advantage of consumers but not to the permanent advantage of farmers. The theory is that, as soon as an improved practice has come into general use, any competitive advantage accruing to those farmers who adopted it first is lost. If this were true, Henry Ford would be out of business. Instead, some hundreds of one-time competitors are gone, but Ford is still a power freshly causing worry to the present gigantic competitors.

The pertinent facts from a farm-management point of view are these:

(1) He who accepts a proved and improved technique before others adopt it gains a competitive advantage, for a time at least (first growers of lespedeza seed).

(2) He who fails to adopt improved techniques is placed at a competitive disadvantage until he does change, and even then he has lost for all time the first profits (hybrid corn).

(3) He who is wide awake and aggressive does not wait to see what long-time effect any one practice may have upon his net income, but is always reaching for another practice that is still better. He knows that he could not compete successfully in modern com-

[4] Ladd Haystead, *Meet the Farmers*, (New York, G. P. Putnam's Sons, 1944), 38.

mercial agriculture if he farmed as his grandfather did. And he knows further that before he becomes the grandfather in the picture, there will be new and better farm practices than he is now using.

But for many farmers there is a joker in this whole trend of farming development. The fast, efficient, high-capacity machinery, the well-laid-out and up-to-date buildings, and the improved and more highly productive livestock all require more and yet more capital investment for each man-job than the average farm business provides. When desired equipment is obtained, the acreage in the farm is often found to be too small to provide full employment for the minimum labor force that must be maintained. More acreage usually means still more capital.

The problem is real and cannot easily be avoided or successfully ignored. Some families would be able to live better if they sold their present inadequate farms and used the capital thus raised to acquire equipment and livestock to operate as tenants on adequate farms.[5]

Without a drastic step such as this, the small-farm business (our definition) may frequently be enlarged. Perhaps an enterprise may be added; for example, chickens. Feed could be purchased if necessary, but the fowl would still add productive employment to aid in more fully utilizing the labor force. Perhaps crops could be intensified by shifting toward kinds that have higher labor returns. Or perhaps additional near-by acreage could be operated along with the home acreage, thus more fully utilizing both labor and equipment. Each of these adjustments takes some capital, the last one usually the least. Each has been and is being made by the operators of small farms, and when wisely done, it serves to reduce overhead per unit of production and to strengthen the competitive position of the whole operation.

The small farm has another place in the sun, one that is being increasingly emphasized and developed; that is, as a home and as part-time employment for the family that likes country life and that has enough off-the-farm employment to provide, between the

[5] See Ladd Haystead, "Not All Tenants Are Jeeter Lester," The Farm Column, *Fortune*, December, 1945, 190.

two, a full-time job. In such cases work away from the farm is an alternative, and frequently a more profitable one, to expanding the farming operations. Henry Ford and some other industrialists have wisely supported a development in this direction for years among their employees. Regardless of its backing and support, this combination method of making a living has such ample merit for many families that it is steadily growing in its own right.

Certain essentials for a successful part-time farm should be recognized, and certain characteristics of this type of farming cannot wisely be ignored. First, one authority has stated: "Our experience is that such farms are often not well operated. The farm interferes with the job and the job interferes with the farm."[6] The part-time farm may be anything from an oversized garden and poultry flock to much more nearly a one-man unit. Clearly it should be adjusted to the kind and amount of off-farm work that is combined with it; or vice versa, the off-farm work should be adjusted to it, depending upon which is the major factor in the breadwinner's employment. Perhaps no more important principle may be advanced than that it should be located where desirable off-farm employment is available and on the sort of all-weather road over which travel to other work is possible at all seasons. In addition, soil, equipment, and labor management are as important to the success of the farming part of the operator's total employment as they are on any other farm.

Then, while love of country life is the motivation of many part-time farming families, the security that the farm provides in times of depression and unemployment is another feature that is commonly stressed. It does have its points—but many a part-time farm cannot readily be changed to a successful full-time farm. When widespread unemployment prevails and the operator turns his full attention to the farm, agriculture is also a depressed industry and he would be under more than normal difficulty in offsetting outside income by more farming.

The part-time farm would provide security in the sense that the family would not have to join a breadline or work on the WPA for necessary food. However, it should not be looked upon as a complete answer to unemployment, for if it would not provide full

---

[6] George Blanch, Utah State Agricultural College, in correspondence with the authors.

employment in good times, it can hardly be expected to do so in bad times. In no sense do we advance this point to discourage would-be part-time farmers, but merely because it is a basic consideration that is best recognized in advance.

Almost without exception persons who are looking for a small farm (their definition) are motivated primarily by a desire for security. The motives expressed in a letter recently received at an agricultural college are typical of thousands of cases:

"Director of Extension
——— College of Agriculture
Dear Sir:

My husband and I have been working in a war plant, and between us have saved $3,000. We hope never to have to repeat the experience of the depression years when there was little work and little income.

We have decided to buy a small farm. Our wants are simple. We wish only a comfortable living and to give our two children an education.

We have been referred to you for information on where we might find a suitable farm. Would you kindly tell us how to go about it?

Very truly yours,

(Mrs.) ——— ———."

This letter, as is quite obvious, came from a city family. When the desires of people such as these are determined, a "comfortable living" is found to mean much the same sort of living that the family has enjoyed from the nonfarm employment from which they accumulated their savings; and further, that an education for their children means college education. A small farm (our definition) does not provide these things.

It is an unpleasant task to disillusion an obviously sincere family—to show them that $3,000 is entirely inadequate capital with which to finance an owner-operated farm with enough good land, equipment, and livestock to accomplish their objectives. Nevertheless, this family unquestionably made a wise move in exploring the situation before they invested in a project that would have little chance to succeed.

"Profits in farming are not large enough to provide a reasonable year's income for six months of work," writes L. S. Hardin of Purdue University,[7] and for most types of farming the results of farm cost-account studies and the experience of able farmers bear him out. "Farming is on a twelve-months' basis; to earn a full income, it is generally necessary to have productive crop or livestock work the year around. If seeking a job in industry, a healthy, ambitious man would not ask for a half-time job. He would want a full-time job with a full income. Yet, some equally healthy and ambitious men have purchased a job for themselves—by buying a farm—and found that the business they could develop would provide only half-time employment, thus half an income."

This statement well expresses the relationship of the farm unit to the operator's job, and it is, in essence, why we have chosen to label a farm "small," without regard to acreage or type of farming, if it does not provide full-time work for one man. It bears repeating that a farmer putting in full time with inadequate equipment and inefficiently laid-out work is actually underemployed, and his production for the year will be too low to permit a fair return for his labor in relation to that of competing, fully employed farmers. This is exactly what has happened to some who have not estimated how much productive work they are accomplishing and who have failed to see their farm as their job.

A cheap farm more often than not means a "cheap" job. If you cannot manage the capital to buy up to your capabilities, consider strongly the advantages of renting, particularly where a reasonable lease may be secured on enough good land. The joys of ownership become tinged with bitterness when the owner realizes that he has bought a job which will keep him in an unsatisfactory rut the rest of his life if he persists in ownership. Translating all capital into better livestock and equipment alone may well raise the family labor returns by an importantly large enough amount over cash or share rent that annual labor income as a renter will far surpass the income under ownership.

---

[7] In correspondence with the authors.

18. Selling Family Farm Labor

IN a farm-management manual prepared for the use of county agricultural agents, S. W. Warren presents the picture of "two farms and how they grew."[1] Diagramatically the story is shown below.

Farm No. 3 was bought and split by the operators of Nos. 1 and 2 when the estate of the former owner was settled. While we believe that the size of a farm cannot be measured in acres (except

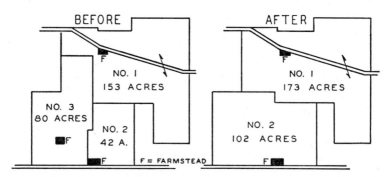

within the narrow limits of equal soil quality and the same type of farming), it does take acres to make a business. These farms are in a dairy region where forty-two acres, the original area of farm No. 2, would definitely be a "grandfather farm." The split was wisely made, in that a major part of the acreage was added to the smaller farm. Yet even now farm No. 2 has less area than would be desirable for a family-commercial dairy farm in the region where these farms are located.

Family-commercial farms are operating units that by one means or another have met the trend of increasing accomplishment per man sufficiently well to keep a minimum of one man productively employed. By no means has it been done in all cases through an increase in acreage. Adjustments, in fact, have taken three forms: the old homestead is operated with fewer hands than formerly, or it is operated more intensively (with greater production)

[1] S. W. Warren, "What Makes a Farm Pay," *Farm Management Manual* (Ithaca, N. Y., Comstock Publishing Company, 1946), 25.

by the same size labor force, or the same size labor force is operating an expanded acreage. As sure as death and taxes, one or more of these adjustments has been made on every farm that has met the trend.

Competition in farming is principally on the side of production costs, and labor is the biggest single cost item. Those farmers who are steadily pushing to the top in labor accomplishment per man, and, in fact, who are ever pushing to new highs, have a maximum opportunity for low costs per pound, per bushel, or per ton. Particularly in the years since World War I have they set a fast pace for others to meet, and they have left a rocky road to profits and good living for those who have not kept up. Inadequate farms have not met the trend, and are being left farther behind by the pace-setters in commercial farming. Unfortunately all family-commercial farms are not in the front rank; they have kept up only in varying degrees.

We recognize that some persons will not accept our concept of a family farm and how it grew. Though our purpose is to look at it and its problems in a commercial setting, others prefer not to view it in this way. There is no characteristic of United States farming that is so constant as its variability. Any one person's attitudes, ideas, and beliefs are generally closely related to the kinds of farms with which he is familiar and the farm people he works with and knows. At one and the same time the family farm has been a foundation, a tradition, and an objective in United States agriculture since Colonial days; "along the same lines as Mother, Old Glory, the Home, and similar safely uncontroversial American ideals."[2] It has become mixed up in politics, and even in a kind of rural-fundamentalist religion. Everyone is for it (including us), only there is no agreement on what the term means. This confusion, too, is merely another result of the changes that have taken place in farming.

At one time "family farm" meant the same to everybody. The farms varied in acres and in the families they supported, but each one was operated to produce what the family used, and the family used (did not sell) what was produced. Now some farms are fully and successfully commercial. Some are operated with commercial intentions but fall far short of success. Others are still subsistence

2 Haystead, *Meet the Farmers,* 131.

farms, producing for use at home, as at one time all farms did. It is the failure to recognize these changes and differences or to define what one means by "family farm" that results in much confusion from the use of the term. Thus it appears that someone should give serious thought to a new and more acceptable terminology. However, when one defines his terms, even though others do not agree with him, at least what is meant becomes clear. Writing in the *Land Policy Review*, Charles S. Hoffman says: "It [a family-type farm] is not so much a unit or a quantity as it is an operating relationship whereby a farm family earns a satisfactory level of living and a substantial degree of security."[3]

Certainly that statement could be accepted by all the widely assorted believers in the family farm. He goes on to say: "It is not a family-type farm if it cannot be operated primarily by family labor, or if its production is considerably above all *minimum requirements and tends toward the commercial-type farm.*"[4]

That is where he would get a schism and an argument, for surely that is not what is meant by a family-type farm by others; say, for example, by Arthur Moore's neighbors in fat McLean County, Illinois.[5] Many believe that the most unique characteristic of United States agriculture is the considerable proportion of all actual farms that are commercial family-operated units.

Mr. Hoffman holds that: "The principle of self-sufficiency, however, is an essential part of the concept of family-type farms." That idea would be laughed out of meeting by the great bulk of Ed O'Neal's Farm Bureau Federation members, but not to the same degree by Jim Patton's Farmers' Union.

The problem, of course, is the degree to which business practice and business principles must be adopted on whatever one calls a "family farm." True D. Morse, among others, has recognized that this is the "Age of Management" in agriculture.[6] He would be the first to say that he is referring to family farms, but does not

<hr/>

[3] "Do You Mean Family Type Farm?" *Land Policy Review*, June, 1945, 25–26.

[4] Italics ours.

[5] See Arthur Moore. *The Farmer and the Rest of Us* (Boston, Atlantic-Little Brown, 1945).

[6] True D. Morse, "Buildings Are Tools," *The Nation's Agriculture*, June, 1945, 7.

mean subsistence units. In essence, this sums up our reason for adopting the "family-commercial" designation.

How big may a family farm be, or how big should it be? We have before us the details of the 1943 operations on a 405-acre farm on the prairies of Illinois. All but 18 acres are in cultivation. The crops consisted of 207 acres of corn, 74 acres of soybeans, 60 acres of oats, 27 acres of hay, and 19 acres of rotation pasture. A hundred and twenty-eight head of feeder cattle put on 42,000 pounds of gain; 165 hogs were raised to 34,000 pounds, live weight.

Land such as this farm is located on is currently selling at $200 or more an acre in this region. Even in the thirties this place was worth $60,000. Livestock, equipment, and working capital add $20,000 more to the total capital being used in the business. Does this get beyond a size that may be called a family-commercial farm?

With two three-plow tractors (no horses), four-row planting and cultivating equipment, an eight-foot combine, a pickup baler, and a corn picker, the farm is being operated by two brothers without hired help at any season of the year. A farm that may be operated by two brothers, a father and son (both able-bodied), or an operator and one regular hired hand, will be accepted by many as a family farm; and the fact that the operation is highly commercial, as in this case, would definitely not exclude it.

Then there is a fruit farm with 100 acres of apples on the shore of Lake Champlain. The capital investment, including the original cost of the farm, the equipment, and the cost of developing the orchards (which are just now coming into full bearing), is a little over $50,000. The labor force includes the operator (who has no sons), one all-year man, one extra man in summer, and seasonal help at harvest.

In 1943, a crop of 39,000 bushels of apples was produced, which, even at the average price for apples in the region over the last ten years, had a value equal to the total capital investment in the business. Is this farm beyond family size?

The labor force could just as well be a father, two sons, and seasonal help for harvesting. The operator certainly thinks of his business as a family unit. And we lean toward agreeing with him.

These are two examples, admittedly on the upper side in size range, of what Arthur Moore has called "large commercial family farms." They are among the family farms that have a maximum opportunity to be successful, because they provide enough business to keep the family labor force occupied at productive work throughout the year. Extra help is used, as needed, at peak seasons. Because of complete mechanization for their respective types of farming, the acreage handled can be, and is, much above average, both per man and in total. The mechanization and full employment at productive work for the regular labor force at all seasons makes possible low unit costs of production.

Certainly, not all farms must have a capital investment equal to these examples to be successful commercial units, but farm-business studies in all parts of the United States have repeatedly shown that the larger farms are the more successful. A summary of the 1944 operations on 434 account-keeping farms in the livestock-grain areas of northwestern Illinois showed higher net operating income for each increase in farm size from 100-acre farms to approximately 500-acre farms (see page 143). The smaller farms were more intensively operated than the larger ones, as shown by the fact that the net earnings per acre were nearly as high in spite of higher costs per acre. But these had too few acres to give the same "leverage" to total operating income that the large farms had. The large farms used more capital per man and used it successfully, as is demonstrated by the comparative rates of earnings on investment.

Some points that should be kept in mind in connection with this illustration are:

1. 1944 was a war-boom year, when farming was unusually profitable and size gave greater leverage to profits than in more normal times.

2. The area in which these farms are located is one of the most productive parts of the Corn Belt, where capital investment per man is much higher than in many other parts of the country. Yet in other areas the difference would merely be one of scaling down the capital per man. The principle remains that a larger investment of wisely used capital per man-job results in higher net labor returns. It is a matter of the quantity of other production factors—land and equipment—that each man has to use.

3. It should not be inferred that because each increase in size shown in this example resulted in higher net operating income, such increases in size could go on indefinitely showing still greater

Farm equipment does not wear out; it rusts out from owner-negligence, as this mower is in the process of doing.

Winter is the time for repairs, such as the replacement of worn
links on this spray rig. When spring spraying time comes around,
this farmer will be ready to go with little worry over breakdowns.

U.S.D.A. PHOTOGRAPH BY KNELL

incomes. These data show only what happened within the size limits that were found. Farms can become unwieldy in size.

4. The larger farms had management that was capable of handling them (as shown by the profits). Management problems increase as farm size increases, sometimes very rapidly. This is particularly true when the labor force increases more rapidly with additions of land and capital than it does in this Corn Belt region. Not a few men have found through hard lessons of experience that they were capable of handling a small- or moderate-sized business successfully but that a larger one was beyond their talents. An admission that this is so would undoubtedly be difficult for any man to make, but most operators who have not had experience with

LARGER FARMS MAKE LARGER PROFITS
Summary of 434 farm businesses in the livestock and grain areas of Northwestern Illinois, 1944[7]

	Total acres per farm				
	Less than 121	121 to 200	201 to 280	281 to 360	361 or more
Acres per farm	102	164	240	323	476
Acres in crops	71	116	165	221	317
Labor force (man-equivalents)*	1.25	1.50	1.77	2.13	2.74
Investment					
Total per farm	$20,004	$31,795	$42,525	$56,740	$73,910
Total per man	$16,003	$21,196	$24,026	$26,638	$26,978
In land, per acre	98.36	103.89	98.19	96.94	92.02
In buildings, per acre	25.51	22.73	19.43	19.10	15.80
In machinery, per acre	16.80	14.00	12.11	10.62	9.35
Expense factors					
Labor cost per crop acre**	$24.69	$18.22	$15.18	$13.57	$12.28
Power and machinery cost per crop acre	13.44	11.13	9.05	9.02	8.35
Buildings cost per crop acre	2.04	1.74	1.52	1.27	1.15
Net earnings per acre	19.12	21.00	20.75	20.85	22.32
Rate earned on investment, per cent	9.7	10.8	11.7	11.9	14.4
Labor and management earnings of the operator	$2,288	$3,211	$4,214	$5,272	$8,351

* Total months of labor divided by 12 to convert to man-equivalents for the year.
** Includes operator and family labor.

[7] Cunningham, Mosher, Searles, and Brown, *Illinois Farm Economics*, July–August, 1945, 254.

large units should probably go slow enough on size increases to test their managerial capacity—to "try their wings," so to speak.

Even stronger evidence on the relation of farm size to labor returns is presented in figures from a study by C. A. Becker of the operating results on 478 farms in northern Livingston County, New York, in 1938. The area is one of the productive soils in which general farm crops and dairy cattle are the predominant enterprises. Farm size, as Becker has measured it, is stated in productive work units (the amount of productive work the farm business provides—see footnote * on page 145).

His figures show (see page 145) that total farm capital and capital per man increased with each increase in the size of the farm business, just as was the case in Illinois. Further, a greater capital investment was accompanied by greater production and a more profitable job for each worker. Some of the interesting comparisons shown by his figures are:

1. That output per man increased with each increase in farm size, and was more than three and one-half times as great on the largest farms as on the smallest ones.

2. After other expenses were paid, the farms with less than 200 productive work units (farms that provided on the average only 135 work units, or half a job per man) failed by $139 to return anything for the work done on them, while larger farms made a return for labor that increased per man with each increase in size.

3. Average wage payments increased with farm size, so that not only an operator but a hired worker as well made more by working on the larger farm. It is also worthy of note that not until output per man reached 15 to 20 per cent above the average for all farms included in the study did labor returns per man equal or exceed the annual wage paid.

4. The operator's return for his own work and management, of course, is reduced if he hires help and pays them more than they produce (note the first of these six size groups), and is proportionately increased if his help produces more than it costs.

The term "labor income" has been used by some farm-management specialists to denote what the farm operator has left for himself after other expenses have been paid. Others have used the term "labor and management wage." In some respects the latter term is preferable because it emphasizes management. So far as physical labor is concerned, most operators can earn only a hired man's wages and are only worth that much from a labor point of

LARGER FARMS HAVE GREATER LABOR RETURNS PER MAN
Summary of 478 businesses in northern Livingston County, New York, 1938[8]

	Total productive work units per farm*					
	Under 200	200 to 399	400 to 599	600 to 799	800 to 999	1,000 or more
Average size, in work units	135	300	476	688	891	1,471
Acres per farm	72	113	167	236	267	432
Acres in crops	37	65	98	134	165	248
Labor force (man equivalents)	1.3	1.5	2.1	2.6	3.4	5.0
Investment:						
Total per farm	$4,811	$8,060	$12,031	$17,318	$21,930	$33,692
Total per man	$3,700	$5,373	$ 5,729	$ 6,661	$ 6,450	$ 6,738
In power and machinery per man	$ 553	$ 881	$ 1,020	$ 1,175	$ 1,077	$ 1,053
Index of output per man	35	76	94	110	118	127
Net returns to labor, total	–$ 139	$ 320	$ 783	$ 1,256	$ 2,207	$ 4,065
Net returns to labor, per man	–$ 107	$ 213	$ 373	$ 483	$ 649	$ 813
Annual wages per man to hired labor**	$ 452	$ 537	$ 553	$ 578	$ 608	$ 652
Operator's labor and management returns after deducting hired and family labor returns at average rate of wage payments	–$ 280	$ 38	$ 181	$ 334	$ 745	$ 1,447

* A productive work unit is that amount of productive farm work (as distinguished from necessary, but not productive, maintenance work) that can be accomplished at an average rate of labor efficiency in a 10-hour day. For example, a dairy cow requires 150 hours of work a year (or 15 work units at average labor efficiency). The total number of work units, so determined, that are provided by a farm business is probably the one best measure of its size, because the employment opportunity on the farm is thus measured in specific terms.

However, a farm worker operating at greater than average efficiency can turn off a work unit in less than 10 hours.

** Includes both wages to hired labor and the value of family labor other than that of the operator.

[8] C. A. Becker, "Farm Management Adjustments, Northern Livingston County, New York, 1908–1938," thesis, Cornell University Library.

view. What they may earn above the going rate of wages is more logically a management return than a labor return.

Management begins with the selection of a farm. In fact, few other management decisions are more important than this one, because the quality and the potential of the operator's job are so greatly influenced by the farm that he chooses to operate. Becker's data, for example, indicate that one would be far better off to use $5,000 of capital for the stock and tools with which to operate a three-man farm business as a tenant than to invest in a small farm unit where he could be the owner. Note that the group of smallest farms included in his study averaged only $4,811 of capital and had a labor force of 1.3 men per farm, although actually there was not enough productive work per farm to provide anything like full employment for one man. Capital earnings were figured at 5 per cent on investment, after which the balance left for labor was a minus quantity of $139. If the operator of the average of these farms had no debts and therefore received for his own use the 5 per cent on capital, his total capital, labor, and management earnings for the year would have been $102.

On the other hand, had he invested his capital in power, tools, equipment, and livestock to operate as a tenant on a three-man farm producing a labor return of about $500 per man, his own capital, labor, and management earnings could have been several times as great.[9] This point seems to be particularly well illustrated by this study simply because 1938 was neither an outstandingly good year nor a bad year.

Still, the operator of one of these small farms—inadequate farms, without question—need not continue in this particular area to operate an inadequate business. Many farmers here, as in the Corn Belt, have become "part-owner" operators by renting land additional to that which they own in order to develop an economic unit of business. Other adjustments, such as those discussed in Chapter 17, might be made, and would be good management in that they would make possible a greater "labor and management wage" to the operator.

Many farm studies have shown that only about one-third of all farm operators earn as much for their own labor and management as the hired hand's wages. This is just about the proportion

[9] See also Chapter 20.

of all farms that are adequate units. Production on other farms—inadequate farms—is too limited to make the operator's job as profitable as the ordinary hired man's job.

Even though the figures from farm-business studies in all parts of the country argue against them, nevertheless, some persons do not look kindly upon suggestions and recommendations for enlarging the average of family-farm businesses. They contend that small businesses with low operating expenses and little need for cash can more easily weather hard times when they come. This argument is for survival rather than for better living on the farms. Subsistence farms may survive also, but they do not keep the boys on the farm. Certainly a retreat may at times be strategic, but we believe with the late General Patton that attack is more often a better form of defense.

To advocate small farm units because of the "stability" that presumably is thereby furnished to agriculture as a whole and to farm families as individual units is merely to argue that when farming must be conducted at a loss, the less business one does, the less he will lose.

The best size of business to operate at a loss is none—whether the business unit in question is a farm or a steel plant.

Becker's study well illustrates this point:

LABOR AND MANAGEMENT WAGE OF THE OPERATOR AS RELATED TO
FARM SIZE AND QUALITY
Summary of 478 farm businesses in
northern Livingston County, New York, 1938[10]

Size of Farm	Performance	Operator's Labor and management wage
Large*	good**	$1,932
Small	good	840
Small	poor	−110
Large	poor	−429

* "Large" and "small" refer to the amount of productive work provided by the farm unit. It should be emphasized that all these "large" farms are within the family-commercial size. They are large merely in relation to the average of the group.

** "Good" and "poor" refer to the level of labor efficiency, the crop yields, and the pounds of milk produced per cow.

10 Becker, "Farm Management Adjustments, Northern Livingston County, New York, 1908–1938."

THE BUSINESS OF FARMING

Note that:

1. The most profitable job for a farm operator in the average sort of year that 1938 was in northern Livingston County, New York, was provided by the farm that was larger than average and on which labor efficiency, crop yields, and livestock production were above average.

2. The best way for an operator to lose money was to operate a larger-than-average farm on which "poor" results were obtained.

3. A small farm, well managed, can make money while the large operation, poorly managed, will fail.

4. The small operation, poorly managed, goes to the wall more slowly merely because, being smaller, it loses less than the bigger unit. Unless very poorly managed, it may never go to the wall in the sense of the operator's being sold out. Particularly if he has no debts and very low cash expense, he may "get by" in a meager sort of way even though a summary of his operations would show year after year that he had received nothing for his labor.

Poor soil, or poorly managed soil, may force farm operations into the red and put a premium on doing a minimum of business rather than a maximum. There is land so unproductive that, from a commercial-operation point of view, the most profitable way to work it is to sit on the porch, because that way one loses the least. Land such as this should not be in commercial operation.

There are depression years, also—1921, 1931, and 1932 are the outstanding examples in recent history—when the less the farmer does, the better off he will be. "It is true," says George Blanch, of the Utah State Agricultural College, "that under conditions of extreme depression the small farm can go further in curtailing cash expenses, and hence, can sometimes survive where larger farms cannot. Yet, this is a relatively unimportant factor in planning farm organization because extreme depression years make up only a small part of the total time, and the lowered efficiency of the small unit is a big price to pay for questionable added security."[11]

The question might well be asked, what security is there in working for nothing, or less than nothing, as Becker found the operators of the small farms included in his study were doing? No alert manager ordinarily makes a capital investment with the

11 In correspondence with the authors.

148

intention of operating it at a loss, or of working for nothing to maintain it. Obviously then, one's objective for normal-time operations (and "normal times" is the most logical basis on which to make plans) should be a business unit that can compete successfully on a cost-of-production basis. The carefully worked-out statistical information available—and there is a great deal of it covering practically every state—indicates that: (1) The minimum-size business that can be expected to pay current wage rates to the operator is the one that provides enough productive work to keep him fully employed; and (2) a still more profitable job, if that be his objective and if he has the requisite management ability, is furnished by a proportionately productive two-, or three-, or four-man unit. Only in periods of deep depression or on unproductive soils is this relationship reversed.[12]

B. D. Parrish and L. J. Norton have reported for a study in Illinois that: "Earnings available to owners and part owners for land purchases [that is, after paying operating expenses, service on debts, and cash living expenses] increased with the size of the farm. For the three-year period [1940–42] the averages for farms of different size, from small to large, were: $189, $731, $877, and $1,824. At these rates it would take the operators in these different groups roughly 52.7, 19.3, 21.0, and 10.8 years, respectively, to accumulate earnings equal to the value of farms of the size they were operating. Expressed another way, this means that the owners and part owners of the largest farms could accumulate in cash the value of the farms they operated in one-fifth the time it would take the owners and part owners of the smallest farms to accumulate the value of their farms.

"Thus, at least in a period of rising prices, it is much easier for an operator of a large farm to buy a large farm from his earnings than it is for the operator of a small farm to buy a small farm from his earnings, and the same can be said for tenants."[13]

Staunch and numerous though the supporters of the "small-farm" ideas may be, the facts do not support their position. A

[12] See A. W. Peterson, M. T. Buchanan, and B. D. Parrish, *"Economic Land Classification in King and Snohomish Counties, Washington, and Its Influence on Full-time Farm Returns* (Mimeographed Bulletin A. E. 5 revised, State College of Washington, 1944); Warren, "What Makes a Farm Pay," in *Farm Management Manual.* Data included in these reports is only representative of many other studies that could be cited.

larger than average family-commercial unit will provide a better living for a family than will a smaller than average unit (assuming of course that it is based upon good soil and good soil management and that it is otherwise well managed), and further, it will provide a greater opportunity to accumulate a worthwhile property over the active lifetime of the operator. The Parrish-Norton study deals with a period when the demand for farm products and consequently the prices at which they sold were rising. A period such as this gives great leverage to the net earning power of the larger farms; but other studies have shown that in much more "normal" times, a larger family-commercial unit is as easy, if not easier, to pay for than a smaller one—simply because, after family living expenses are deducted from the net income of the smaller farm, there is a smaller balance available with which to increase the operator's equity. Moreover at the end of whatever time it takes to pay for the farm, the larger unit represents a greater capital accumulation. (Any farm, even when well managed, will have its poor years resulting from unavoidable crop failure or "price failure." And on a large farm the resulting losses can be greater than on a small farm. Yet presumably the farmer, like any other businessman, would set aside reserves from fat years to carry over those that are lean.)

Non-farm workers can live and accumulate property in proportion to how good their jobs are and what they earn. In that respect farmers are no different. The farm business that the farmer operates sets the limits on his potential job. How well he manages determines what he does with that potential. However he may choose to use his earnings, his family can live only in proportion to his income. Furthermore, the trend in farming developments makes a productive farm more and more necessary. Rates of production per man that are good enough to meet competition today may not be good enough in the years ahead, simply because the trend is continuing.

[13] B. D. Parrish and L. J. Norton, *Financial Position of a Representative Group of McHenry County Farmers, 1940–42* (Illinois Agricultural Experiment Station Bulletin 512, June, 1945), 560.

"Large farms," as the term is used by Parrish and Norton, does not mean farms beyond the family-commercial size. Their "large-farm" group averaged about 3-man to 3.5-man businesses, and had an average investment of a little over $33,000, compared to $15,000 investment and a man-equivalent of one to one and a half workers in their "small-farm" group.

19. Big-business Farm Labor

IF a larger than average family-commercial unit is desirable, why stop size increases within limits that would be classed as a family unit? The larger than average unit has its great advantage in providing more land and more equipment per man than the smaller farm provides. And these, properly used, serve to boost production per man, which has been shown necessary to meet and to stay ahead of the production trend. Ever more land and equipment per man-job appears to be another trend that on successful farms is nearly keeping pace with increasing labor productivity.

It has been a realization of just this change in the desirable land–equipment–labor balance that has led to the belief in some quarters that United States farming is headed toward large-scale units of operation—most commonly referred to as "corporation farms." Certain facts give credence to this belief; others, of which the labor-management problem is most important, do not.

"Big business" is what is usually meant by corporation farming; it is immaterial whether ownership is corporate, partnership, or individual. The distinguishing characteristics of farm units so designated are primarily the relations between management and labor. On a family-commercial farm, even one employing several hired hands, the operator and possibly other family workers remain a part of the working force. Thus the operator is both worker and manager. On a large-scale farm (our definition) the number of hired workers is beyond the number that a manager who is himself a part of the labor force can supervise. Thus, management, whether hired or furnished by the owner, is "white collar," and the whole relationship between management and labor tends to change character from that which prevails where the manager works right along with the hired hands.

Those who extol unreservedly the virtues of large-scale farming say in essence: "Commercial farming is a business that, like any other business, will succeed or fail on the business principles applied to it. Since it is a business, the efficiencies of the big-business unit give it that much more chance to succeed." The first part of this statement is entirely correct and we would not detract from it in the least. The second part may not be so generally true, because the hoped-for efficiencies depend upon management.

H. S. Tyler, in a summary of between eleven and twelve thousand farm-business records, found that labor efficiency per man increases rapidly from less-than-one-man farms up to three- and four-man farms and then tends to level off, showing no further increase with additional size.[1] More than anything else it is the high labor accomplishment per man that may be obtained on the properly equipped and managed farm that makes it possible to hire labor, pay current wages, and make a profit above wages paid. Yet in many types of farming a large labor force is difficult to supervise, and the necessary rate of production per man becomes proportionately difficult to attain. It takes a good manager to supervise properly three or four men, and an increasingly better one to supervise more. That, in brief, is the major handicap of the big-business farm.

Agriculture is a biological business. Considerate, intelligent, and "interested" care of living, growing things is essential to its success. The expression "a green thumb" is frequently used to designate an elusive, magical quality that results in plants' and animals' putting all out for those who possess it. Yet, a green thumb is no mystery. It is self-sacrificing care and intuitive insight into what to do and when to do it, to make plants and animals respond just a little better, and always a little better still. It is the art of farming in its highest form, or the science of farming in successful practice. It requires a devotion to the job that wages do not ordinarily buy. It is that love of the work and the animals that is demonstrated by one more trip to the barn "just for a look around" before climbing the stairs to bed. It is the willingness to stay up all night at farrowing or lambing time, or to get up in the night, or, even more, a reluctance to leave the pens at all.

No implication is intended that these self-sacrifices are a daily occurrence on the successful farm. They are in fact and practice more rare than commonplace. But it is the willingness—indeed, the eagerness—with which they are accepted that denotes the true meaning of the word "husbandman." Commercial as farming may become, accounting controlled though it may be, its biological nature remains, and plants and animals will respond to this kind of care. And this kind of care they frequently do not get at critical

[1] H. S. Tyler, *Factors Affecting Labor Incomes on New York Farms* (Cornell Extension Bulletin 401, 1939).

times when the manager works at a desk and does not give it himself.

It would be too sweeping to imply that such devotion to the job cannot be hired, but it cannot usually be hired in volume. He who possesses it, and any business talent along with it, will ordinarily become a farm operator in his own right. No, this talent is not always present on family-operated farms, though if one looks, it will almost invariably be found lurking in the background on successful ones.

Large numbers of workers are best controlled with a time clock and close supervision. They work most successfully with inert materials and mechanical contrivances. They are most easily "managed" when they are under quota production of goods coming from simple, repetitive processes. All of these conditions are completely unlike most farming, where the job may change from hour to hour.

Not at all strangely, big factory "farms" come closest to duplicating this system. The majority of the present small number of truly large-scale farms, for example, are in specialized types of farming with simple repetitive techniques. They are in fruit or vegetable operations where gang labor may be closely supervised; in the seed or nursery businesses, or in retail milk production, where marketing is actually the major function and marketing margins may help to carry rather high production costs; in wheat farming, where large machines with comparatively small crews can provide all the labor needed to balance a large capital investment; or in livestock ranching, in which the relation of man power to capital is similar.

Historical performance, of at least the units he knew, has led one wag to say that large-scale farms may be divided into two classes; "those that have failed," and "those that will fail." A statement such as this may be widely quoted, but it need not be true, as consistent money-making units in the types of farming listed above serve to demonstrate.

Truly, accumulations of capital beyond the ability of most individuals to match do have advantages in farming—mostly in buying and selling efficiency and in assuring a desirable balance of land and equipment to labor. But so much of the very essence of farming success lies in production that these advantages are commonly offset in the more general types of crop and livestock agriculture. Successful low-cost production depends upon the efficient performance of the biological factors involved—the plants and the animals. An interest that is directly related to the success of the enterprise—more closely than a pay check—is generally necessary to get the desired results. The rapidity with which hens can die, or the failure of feeder stock to translate feed into efficient gain, or crop waste in the field when the whole job is left to laxly supervised, run-of-the-mill hired hands is only too common tragedy. Net-production efficiency falls, and the operating balance for the year can be a sorry figure.

All that has been said before about land, equipment, and labor management and all that fills the following pages is predicated upon a base of successful, intelligent plant and animal care. This is the foundation of farming, upon which successful business management is only a superstructure, and without which no amount of capital, large or small, may be successfully employed.

Many who would have translated farming solely into dollars-and-cents financial statements without proper knowledge of or attention to this indispensable foundation have failed, and this neglect has been uppermost in the difficulties of large-scale farms. It has led directly to statements on probable failure such as the one quoted above. Yet by no means does this imply that all large-scale farms will fail. Whether or not they will succeed depends upon management talent. The large-scale farm, primarily because of the character of the relationship between the management and the labor force, presents an especially great management problem in getting the proper response from plants and animals to make possible the necessary production per man. It appears to be true in many types of farming that management skill must increase in approximate geometric ratio to increases in the size of the farm business. Particularly is this true of the multiplicity of little problems that add up to be the total labor-management problem. A lack of management talent interested in the jobs will probably more than anything else limit the growth in numbers of truly large-scale farms.

The reputed advantage of big-business farms in buying and selling and in hiring specialists is at least in part offset by the increasing availability to family-commercial units of well-managed buying and selling co-operatives and of technical assistance through the Agricultural Extension Service. With these services at his call and with sound production and business management on his farm, the family-commercial operator need have no fear that big-business farming will out-compete him. He can himself set a pace of competition that a majority of large-scale farms (our definition, still) will be hard pressed to meet. He has more reason to fear that other aggressive family-commercial operators may step up their efficiency and produce more cheaply than he than that the colossi of the fields will force him out of business.

20. Rent Land—Sell Labor Higher

A FARM changes hands and must be refinanced at least every generation. Only the small number of farms that are incorporated units, for which stock certificates may be shifted in varying proportions to different owners, avoid that every-generation problem of refinancing. Even farms that pass from father to son, and a relatively small proportion of all farms do, must usually be financed by the new owner, who more often than not inherits only a part-interest and must buy out other heirs. The problem lies in the fact that a young man may reach physical maturity and accumulate the experience necessary to be a successful farmer before he has attained a financial competence that enables him to finance adequately a farm business.

One of the difficulties when farming is chosen as a livelihood is that the farmer must finance his own job, in direct contrast to factory work or most other jobs. When good land could still be homesteaded, when a few head of livestock and some simple, inexpensive tools provided all that was needed to start farming, a young man faced no such problem as he does today.

An adequate one-man farm has come to require from $5,000 to $20,000 of capital, depending upon the type of farming and the region in which one locates; and units providing greater employment opportunity require an almost proportionately greater investment. Certainly, one can buy some sort of job as a farmer with a smaller capital, but let us emphasize that we are concerned with an adequate job—with enough land, equipment, and working

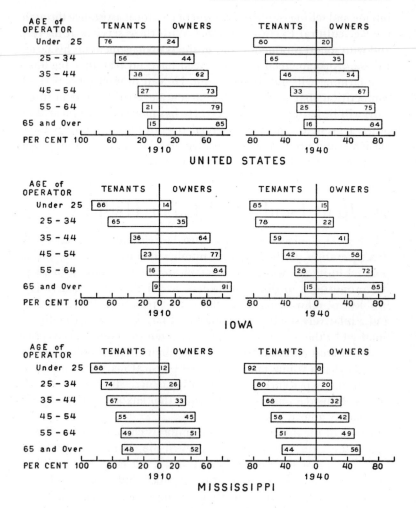

Proportion of Tenant Operators and Owner Operators, 1910 *and* 1940

The proportion of all farm operators who were tenants is shown by the figures on the left side of the bars, and the proportion who were owners by the figures on the right side of the bars. In recent years the transition from tenant to owner status has taken longer than it did before World War I, but it is accomplished by about as large a proportion of all farmers now as then.

156

capital per man to provide an adequate, if not indeed a maximum, opportunity for the labor that goes into the operation. This need becomes obvious when success on the farm is measured in the net return to labor. The productive capacity of the labor force, both gross and net, is either limited or multiplied by the quantity, quality, and management of the capital-requiring production resources with which it works.

Fortunately, one need not have in hand the full capital requirements for a successful farm in order to start farming. If he has stock and tools and a part of his real-estate capital, the balance may be financed on a mortgage. But even a mortgage requires sound management, for mortgages have been both boon and doom to farm families in endless numbers. Anyone who, either through ignorance or error, should find himself farming poor soils (meaning soils that are a limiting factor in successful production) should ordinarily have no mortgage at all. He would more than likely have problems enough in producing a living for his family without being saddled with mortgage interest and payments.

Studies made in various parts of the country by the Farm Credit Administration have shown that on an adequate farm of productive land a mortgage of one-half, two-thirds, or even three-quarters of the real-estate value (more debt is justified as the quality of the land increases) is ordinarily easier to pay off than a much smaller mortgage on a poorer farm—all of which is to say again that one can never get very far away from his dependence upon the productivity of the soils he uses.

And on the subject of the size of a farm in relation to its capacity to carry and pay a mortgage, both Becker's data (Chapter 18, page 145) and the information presented from the Parrish-Norton study (Chapter 18, page 149) may be interpreted to show that the larger farm unit may both carry a bigger mortgage and pay it faster. The question is merely: How much is left after paying operating expenses? In other words, how much does the family have from which to live and to retire their debts? The answer is: More on a productive farm than on an unproductive one, and, except in periods of deep depression, more on a larger than average unit than on one smaller than average.

To be an owner-operator, yes, and to have his farm free of debt, is the traditional objective of the United States farmer, not of every one, perhaps, but at least of the great majority. The difficulty that stands between many farm families and that objective is the capital needed to accomplish it. A common result is to take an owner status too soon, before capital accumulations are sufficient to finance an adequate farm. Just owning "a farm" is not enough. If the family must live on the income from the farm, the objective should be a farm that will provide an adequate job and, through that, an adequate living. Too much haste in becoming an owner or failure to recognize the consequences of taking on an inadequate farm has led to many mistakes.

Probably the experience of one farmer of our acquaintance has been repeated many times. Very likely it is equally true that not many have had the fortitude that this man showed in correcting his mistake. He had been a tenant-operator for some years on a good 200-acre farm and had saved enough to buy an 80-acre farm with a mortgage; and thus to accomplish the transition from tenant on the land of another to owner-operator of his own land. Yet, over a period of three years, he became a progressively more unhappy owner-operator. The 80 acres in corn, hay, small grain, and livestock were not enough to keep him and his son fully employed. After two years the son went to work as a hired hand on another place, and the father worked alone.

Three years were enough. The fourth year the farmer rented the place he owned for enough cash to about cover taxes, insurance, and interest; his son came back to work with him, and he became a tenant-operator again on a 240-acre farm about five miles from the one he owned. Here there was enough productive work to keep both men employed and to return a better income to the operator as a tenant than he had been able to net on his own inadequate farm.

After two years, the young man to whom he had rented his 80-acre unit decided to move. The owner's first intention was to rent to someone else. What he finally did was to operate the acreage himself along with the 240 acres he worked as a tenant. (He had acquired some rubber-tired equipment that could be moved easily from one farm to the other, making this decision practical.) Thus, within a period of six years he moved (1) from tenant to owner—a bad move because he bought an inadequate farm; (2) from owner back to tenant—a good move because of the more

These teen-age Rush County, Indiana, youngsters, plus the machines, provide needed seasonal labor while continuing their education. Machines increase their work output many times over.

Where a crop does not lend itself to mechanization, as in the case of the strawberries shown here near Gresham, Oregon, a large and assured supply of migrant or seasonal laborers is essential to success. High school boys and girls are favored on the West Coast.

adequate job the rented farm provided; and (3) from tenant-operator to part-owner-operator—which, because he is a good enough manager to handle both places successfully, was the best move.

Much has been said and written in criticism of United States farm tenancy in recent years, and certainly, compared to an ideal of owner operation for all farmlands, it has its disadvantages. Yet, as we have already pointed out, the principal reason that complete owner operation does not prevail is that the physical capacity and experience to be a farm operator are usually attained earlier in life than is the capital accumulation necessary to be a farm owner. Tenancy, as a step to farm ownership, is by no means an unmitigated evil. Without tenancy "many young farmers would be operating farms too small for their energies, and many old farmers would have in hand far more land than they could use advantageously, to the loss of the young farmer, the old farmer, and the people of the nation who consume farm products."[1]

Fears and opinions have been expressed that tenancy as a step to farm ownership in the United States is breaking down, to become, in increasing degree, tenancy for life. Available facts do not bear out this contention. Rather, the evidence is that the transition to ownership has been delayed; that, in recent years compared to a generation ago, tenants have operated for a longer time as tenants before becoming owners; but that among those who spend a lifetime at farming, the proportion that reach ownership status did not change greatly between 1910 and 1940. This fact is borne out by the figures not only for the United States as a whole, but also for Iowa, representative of the Corn Belt, and for Mississippi, representative of the Cotton Belt. Tenancy is still a steppingstone toward ownership, except, of course, on the "cropper" units of the South, where it neither has been nor ever will be.

"There has been a tendency among students of the tenancy problem," says P. L. Poirot, "to over-emphasize the undesirable features sometimes associated with tenancy. Tenants have been blamed for overproduction, soil depletion, agricultural depression, low morals, inferior standards of living, and numerous other evils, whose cure would lie in the abolition of tenancy. Much of this work might have been more constructive if the existent amount

[1] H. C. Taylor, *Outlines of Agricultural Economics*, Revised Edition (copyright 1919, 1925, and 1931 by The Macmillan Company, New York), 326.

of tenant operation had been accepted, and more attention devoted to the improvement of landlord-tenant relationships.

"The American theory of tenancy is that it constitutes one of the rungs on the 'agricultural ladder.' The assumption is that a farmer becomes a tenant as a step toward the goal of farm ownership. If that assumption is correct, then any increase in the per cent of tenancy must mean, (1) that more men are using this step because it seems to be the best way to proceed, (2) that men must remain tenants longer in order to accumulate the increased capital necessary for ownership, or (3) that fewer men are eventually able to rise above the economic status of a tenant. Those men who are tenants for the third reason are the ones who introduce complications to the tenancy problem. Unfortunately, not every tenant is a potential owner. The ladder for some men ends with the tenant step.

"There are two rather distinct groups of these permanent tenants. In one group fall those men who lack the managerial ability to operate a business of their own. They may do an excellent job of farming under the guidance of a good landlord, but fail miserably if charged with the responsibility of ownership. As a rule, however, they are only fair farmers and poor business men. Some of them have been owners for a time but have slipped back to the position of tenants.

"To the other group of permanent tenants belong those men who have the ability but lack the desire to become owners. They are all successful farmers who feel that they are as well off to be renting as they would be if they were paying taxes and upkeep on a farm of their own. This second group of tenants does not constitute a problem. So long as there are landlords willing to rent to them, and so long as they continue to do a good job of farming, society will not suffer because of them. English agriculture has survived several generations under such a system. Most of the English farmers are tenants. They are good farmers, but prefer to invest their savings in operating capital, leaving the land ownership to another class of people.

"The farm tenants of the United States that are a problem group are those unable to get out of the tenant class because of

2 "A Study of Rented Farms in New York with Emphasis on Rental Agreements," thesis, Cornell University Library, 1940.

inferior managerial ability. Men of that type are to be expected in almost every occupation. The whole institution of tenancy should not be condemned because some tenants are unsuccessful."[2]

With that summary of the much-debated tenancy question, we concur. And we therefore forthrightly commend tenancy on an adequate farm instead of ownership of an inadequate unit, where, because of lack of capital, a family faces these alternatives.

The evidence that supports this position extends over a very long period. In his standard text, *Outlines of Agricultural Economics,* Henry C. Taylor quotes from an article that was published in England in 1804, entitled "The Bad Consequence of a Farmer Lessening his Capital by Purchase of Land."[3] The article points out that one can be more successful financially by investing a given sum of money ($£2,000$ is used in the illustration) in stock and equipment to operate rented land than to buy his own farm. Why? Because he would be able to finance a larger business and thus provide himself with a more profitable job.

Parrish and Norton bring this same type of evidence up to date.[4] They show that the total capital investment in fifty-seven tenant-operated McHenry County, Illinois, farms in 1942 earned a 13.8 per cent return; but the tenants' working capital earned 33.4 per cent, while the landlords' real-estate investment earned 7.3 per cent. The following figures from their study are of further interest:

FARM SIZE[5]
(measured by the number of productive work units)

	Under 400	400–549	550–699	700 and over
Total investment	$15,255	$19,439	$25,775	$39,321
Rate earned on total investment	7.5%	12.7%	14.2%	15.5%
Rate earned on operator's investment	17.9%	32.4%	33.2%	37.5%
Rate earned on landlord's investment	4.4%	5.6%	7.2%	9.1%
Operator's labor and management wage	$ 1,299	$ 2,183	$ 2,800	$ 3,629

In interpreting the Parrish-Norton data, it is important that the method of calculation is understood. First, in arriving at the

3 Page 366.
4 *Financial Position of McHenry County Farmers.*
5 Page 571.

rate earned on investment, all expenses were deducted to determine the balance, which was called "capital earnings." Second, to figure labor income, or labor and management wage, all expenses were deducted from gross income and then interest on all capital used in the business (figured at a uniform rate such as 5 per cent) was deducted to arrive at a balance, which was called the "operator's earnings" for his work and management.

Results of studies on the subject seem to justify this conclusion: While significantly greater income is earned by working capital than by real estate capital, the more important consideration to the operator is that a given amount of capital, invested in the stock and tools necessary to operate a larger than average farm as a tenant, will give him a much more profitable job than the same capital invested in a smaller, less adequate farm on which he could be an owner-operator.

It is after reasoning from just such evidence as the elaborate array presented above that we say: RENT! If your capital is a limiting factor in acquiring a farm that will provide a job adequate to your talents, use it first to get the equipment that will multiply the efficiency of your labor. Then use the labor and equipment on rented land until you can be owner-operator of an adequate farm.

There are many farms to rent, some held by retired farmers, some by widows, and some (an increasing number in many parts of the country) by that group of people known as absentee landlords, who have a farm only as a place to invest money. Perhaps, also, there are many tenants to rent them, but the landlord group says repeatedly that the problem is to get good tenants. After looking over some of rural America, one is led to observe that some landlords might get and hold better tenants if they would improve their places a little, particularly the houses, so that the right kind of tenant families would be contented to live in them. Some might thereby get good enough tenants to more than pay the cost through increases in production. (The installation of a pressure water system is No. 1 on the list. Note that this increases farm production and reduces costs, as well as making a more satisfied tenant.)

A tenant-landlord relationship is, after all, a partnership. Both parties should want "good" arrangements. No small part of the tenancy problem has been rental agreements, or a lack of them, that failed to give encouragement to both sides of the partnership to build up and improve the farm. Much thought has recently been given to the problem. County agricultural agents and state agricultural colleges are both willing and able to furnish assistance on rental arrangements and to provide suitable rental forms. What is really important, however, is that no partnership arrangement or rental form is any good unless both parties honestly try to make it work.

21. Hired Labor

THE HIRED MAN

NEARLY everyone wants a good hired man. A "cheap" man usually is not worth his lower wages. Within a few miles of each other in the Lake Region fruit belt are two farmers who illustrate the extremes on this topic. One always has three or four men around a place where the amount of work to be done indicates that only one, or at the most two, should be needed. But he has the kind of men two or three of whom are required to do one man's work.

With farming steadily becoming more specialized, more scientific, and more complicated, a chuckle-headed hired man is a handicap rather than a benefit. Modern commercial farming is no place for the incompetents just because they come cheap.

The other farmer believes that "a few extra dollars buy a lot more man.

"I'm paying that fellow $80 a month and privileges," he said. "No one else around here is paying more than $60. [That, of course, was before the war.] But he's an unusual kind of man to whom you can turn over a spraying crew and know that the trees will be properly sprayed and the equipment properly cared for.

"I hired a fellow one time," he went on, "and sent him out to drag the orchards. He caught the harrow on the first tree, missed the next two by four feet leaving a big strip of weeds, and then hung up on the fourth one. We got him started again and he zigzagged down the rest of the row and dumped the tractor in the drainage ditch at the end. That kind of help I can't use."

His decision was understandable, although one might raise a question about the amount of training he had given the man before setting him at a job with which he was unfamiliar. Perhaps at one time it was not necessary for the farmer to spend much time training his help, but that situation seems now to be changing. There are many new and technical jobs to be done on the farm, and new ways to do old jobs. No hired man should be expected to do, by instinct, tasks that he has not done before. Simply because he comes "with experience" does not mean that he knows how a certain farmer does his work or wants it done. The right kind of hired man wants to do right; the simplest concept of good management indicates that the farmer has a responsibility to see that he does.

The best kind of hired man is the one who is actually an apprentice farmer, who is going on up the agricultural ladder. Often a farmer cannot hold a man like this as long as he would like, but while he has him, he has good help. Whether this type of man is married or single, he wants to work for a good farmer because he wants good experience. If he is married, he has another major interest, or at least his wife has: the living quarters that are provided. Seldom is it difficult to get a good man if a comfortable, modern house is available for his family to live in.

Just outside of a city that was in the front ranks of the war-boom towns, is a farmer who has a reputation among his neighbors for doing the right thing at the right time. He always says it is "just luck." One smart move, that may or may not have been just lucky, he made in 1941 when he modernized his tenant house, putting in furnace and bath. (It already had electricity.)

As much as anything else it was that house which attracted to his farm a young couple, the husband, he has said, the best man he ever had on the farm. He paid good wages, but war plants paid better. At the end of the 1942 season, the hired man thought he could get ahead faster if he quit and went to work in the city, but his wife would not leave the house. Consequently, throughout the war period, when any kind of replacement help would have been hard to find, this farmer held an excellent man because he had a good house for him—no, for his wife—to live in.

And a final point on the question of wages: The farmer is interested in the produce-cost of his hired help because he sells produce to get the dollars with which to pay the wage bill. The hired man is interested in what the economist calls the "real value" of his wages, that is, what they will buy, because first his living and then his savings come from what he gets.

Thus, the farmer has to sell produce to get wage dollars, and the hired man (a married man) has to buy produce to eat. Whatever produce the farmer could furnish to the hired man from the farm in part-payment of wages is worth wholesale price to him with no marketing costs. Whatever produce the hired man can get from the farm at wholesale price replaces purchases at retail prices, and thus adds to his real wages.

"Privileges" to a married man are, of course, traditional, but with privileges so much to the advantage of both the farmer and the man, it seems strange, and actually poor management, that so little attention is given on many farms to making maximum use of the variety and quantity of privileges that might be furnished. Many good managers held some highly desirable men right through the war years by providing desirable living quarters and a maximum amount of privileges that helped to reduce their living costs. The plan worked in wartime, and it is also good management in peacetime. Such treatment might, on occasion, hold that rare kind of hired man a farmer can ill afford to lose.

The principles of good labor management as applied to the hired man are no different from those for family labor. Paying substandard wages is seldom, if ever, the way to the most efficient use of hired help. A far more successful method would seem to be: (1) Provide living and working conditions that will attract and hold the best possible men; (2) provide farm organization and work methods that will permit and encourage the help to accomplish a high rate of production, from which it will be possible—and in the end, profitable—to pay a little more than the neighbors pay; (3) use the same principles on the family labor, and it will be easier to compete with the offerings of the city.

SEASONAL LABOR

Farming is an industry in which the sun and the seasons dictate the timing of the work. Planting and harvest times bring seasonal peaks of labor needs—peaks that are a limiting factor in the size of farm that a given labor force can handle and in the total annual production that they can accomplish. Fast and efficient machines can and have reduced some of these peaks, but not all of them. Particularly have seedbed preparation, planting, and cultivating been mechanized. However the final and all-important job of bringing in the harvest still requires upwards of a million and a half seasonal workers,[1] employed mostly in harvesting fruits, vegetables, sugar beets, cotton, and other specialty crops.

Probably seasonal labor can never be eliminated entirely from all types of farming, although farmers would be glad to eliminate it if they could. Often it is difficult to obtain at the proper time, much that has to be used is unskilled, frequently undependable, and sometimes difficult to handle, and the success of a whole season's work in crop production is all too often at its mercy. That being the situation from the farmers' point of view, it is small wonder that they have worked untiringly to obtain equipment that would reduce the harvesting peaks of their labor needs.

Nor is the situation a satisfactory one from the seasonal workers' point of view. If they could, many would find other work, just as they did during the war period. Though the wage rates may be good and all the farmer can afford to pay, the work is of necessity irregular, and annual earnings may be distressingly low. For migrants, living units can hardly be the best when they must be maintained by the farmer for very short periods of occupancy each year. If the economic system of the country could provide other opportunities for these people, there would seem to be a great advantage, other than to farmers alone, in promoting machine developments to replace this harvest labor.

Some farmers avoid a seasonal labor problem by maintaining a high degree of diversity in the farm operation. Other things being equal, this is desirable when possible. A farmer whose cost accounts are on hand well illustrates this advantage. One hundred and twenty acres of cropland are used for a six-year rotation of corn, cabbage, beans, wheat, alfalfa, alfalfa. Another fifteen acres are in apple orchard. These crops provide a sequence of work through the growing and harvesting seasons. Corn and beans are planted, the first cutting of alfalfa is harvested, the cabbage acreage is set, and the wheat is harvested. After a short respite, a second cutting of alfalfa is gathered, beans are harvested and wheat planted, apples are picked, and the cabbage and corn harvested. Sev-

[1] From mimeographed reports on farm labor issued periodically by the U.S.D.A., Bureau of Agricultural Economics.

eral of these jobs follow close upon one another, but they do not come all at once.

The livestock on the farm consists of 15 fall-freshening dairy cows, 200 ewes bred to lamb in March, 1,600 hens with the pullets started early enough to go into the laying house during the slack crop-work period of late July and early August, 50,000 baby chicks hatched, with the incubators started at Christmas time, and 500 turkey poults raised to mature for the Thanksgiving trade.

With this diversity of crop and livestock enterprises, there is productive work at all seasons of the year. The labor force of four men is kept busy at all times; they accomplish a total of production far greater than they could turn out if the same amount of work were less uniformly distributed.

This farm is exceptional in its diversity and labor distribution. On farms with greater limitations of climate, soil, or market opportunity, a program such as this would not be possible. On smaller farms, even with similar opportunities, this diversity might quickly result in uneconomically small enterprise units.

Perhaps the best management of seasonal labor is to eliminate it from your operation if possible. If that cannot be done, you must use it, and your success will be related to how well you manage it. "All of us know that labor is at a premium right now," said C. G. Bradt in 1944. "But have you also stopped to think that good labor management commands an even higher premium? That means, a good boss will get work done where a poor boss will fail."[2]

22. Key Labor-management Principles

MATCHING the size of the farm business to the available labor supply, so that labor is fully and effectively employed, is the essence of labor management. When labor is not fully employed, net farm income is lower than it should be. The trouble will probably be found to lie in an inadequate farm. When labor is fully employed and farm income is still too low, it means that the labor is not being applied effectively. Look for the fault in:

A. *Size of Business:* The "size" of soil productiveness is too low, the acreage size too small, the number of livestock units is

2 C. G. Bradt, *Farm Labor* (Cornell Extension Letter, July, 1944).

less than farm carrying capacity, the machine capacity is inadequate, building design or capacity is faulty, or working capital is too small, and so on.

B. *Labor Methods:* A full day's work is not producing enough income units because (1) there is too much waste motion in doing chores (carrying water is the most expensive job on the farm, feed storage is not close enough to hoppers or bunkers, manure removal is inefficient because of structure design, operator is carrying his work to livestock instead of making livestock bring work to him, and so on; (2) there is waste motion in field work, such as too short rows, tool hitches are unwieldy and time wasting, seed and fertilizer have not been distributed correctly for refilling hoppers, or obsolete tools are wasting time in haying; (3) too many job changes are made in one time-period (trips to town were not anticipated and consolidated, or cultivating, late seeding, haying, and summer plowing were each given part of the day).

C. *Planning:* The best operators know their rotation years in advance and make allowance for the unforeseen, such as weather breaks, at least weeks in advance. Then, each night, the most productive hour of the day is put in while the operator plans what he will do the following day if the weather is good, if it is bad, if a machine breaks, or if someone he depends upon does not perform as expected. Farmers who work by rule of thumb say that planning of this sort is futile because the unplanned is the common occurrence in farming. Oddly enough, these farmers are the ones who have endless hard luck, while the planners seem somehow to get along better, even with the same bad breaks in weather, machinery, disease, or acts of God. The close observer notes that they never waste time, are never at a loss to make the next move the instant something goes wrong, and have made ample provision in advance for alleviating any unfortunate circumstance that might appear. For instance, they are the farmers who utilize an otherwise wasted winter day to replace the worn parts in their machinery.

Being one's own boss looks most attractive from the outside; but if that status is to bring success and contentment instead of failure and bitterness, the quality of the bossing has to be on as high a plane as that of other farm operators on successful farms of similar size and quality. Otherwise, the less successful operator will find himself becoming one of those neighborhood pests who ascribe every fortunate circumstance on the other fellow's farm to "merely fool's luck" while every bad circumstance on their own farms becomes "unavoidable bad luck." Despite the chancy character of farming, today we have so vast a pile of data on all types of farms and farmers that any sober student must realize that luck plays a much less important role than has been thought heretofore. Further, we know that those men who are the best managers seem to draw more "lucky breaks" to themselves than those who are poor managers. Management means not just learning to operate under ideal conditions, but, even more, doing all those things which will bring all conditions under as much control as possible, and then taking full advantage of opportunistic variables while discounting in advance and offsetting the negative variables. In other words labor management begins with managing oneself and winds up with properly managing the labor of others.

In conclusion, we refer to H. P. McFeeley of Rutgers, who quotes a very pertinent thought from Kipling:

> *I keep six honest serving men*
> *(They taught me all I knew.)*
> *Their names are Why, and What, and When*
> *And Where, and How, and Who.*[1]

There is a good idea in this verse for the farm operator, or anyone else, with a certain task to perform. *Why* do I do this job the way I am doing it? *What, When, Where,* and *How* could I change the way I do it to make the work easier, the accomplishment greater, or the cost lower? *Who* is going to figure out something better if I don't?

It is human nature to resist change, because old habits, like old shoes, are comfortable. The path of least resistance is to do things the old way, but the old way may not win in fast competition. A farmer gets paid for his productive work, if his rate of accomplishment is high enough to leave him any pay. Possibly by the old way it takes two hours of work on his cows to produce a hundredweight of milk. Possibly by asking *why, what, when, where,*

[1] H. P. McFeeley, *More Work with Less Effort* (New Jersey Agricultural Experiment Station and U.S.D.A. co-operating, Mimeographed Bulletin, August, 1945), 14.

how, and *who,* and then doing something about the answers, he could cut the time to one hour. Maybe if he did that, he would not have to hire help and the labor return could all be his. For whom is he running his farm, anyway?

PART IV: Farm Organization

"The real problem is management. Land, equipment, labor, livestock, and production supplies are just crazy-quilt pieces until put together in a well-balanced pattern."

23. Higher Price or Lower Cost?

ALMOST as dog-eared and worn-with-use as the little farm *vs.* the big farm controversy is the perennial question of self-sufficing *vs.* commercial farming. Despite the sometimes acrimonious discussion among almost everybody (except actual farmers on the land), the long-time trend has been steadily toward the commercial. The farm production of the country is now more than 85 per cent for commercial purposes—as indeed it must be for a domestically fed population that is more than four-fifths nonfarm.

Quite apart from the philosophical angles to this trend are the practicalities. Paul A. Johnstone presents the history of one Iowa farm and probes the meaning of some of the broadly significant changes through which it went. The particular farm is the quarter-section where his grandparents had lived a good and secure life throughout the latter half of the last century, but from which a more recent owner had bowed out to the sheriff.

"Let me emphasize," said Johnstone,[1] "that as far as I can judge, the man who lived a contented lifetime of unthreatened security on that farm was no better a man, and no better a farmer, than the one who later lost it. The times had changed, not the quality of the men.

"I suppose Grandfather was really very far from being a highly efficient farmer. He never bought good seed except for a very few things, like clover. Mostly, he saved his own seed each year. His sires were far from being prize winners. He would never plant

1 "Grass Roots and Far Horizons," *Land Policy Review*, December, 1940, 5.

potatoes in the light of the moon, and he had many other superstitions. He hated the idea of banks and credit. Of all his tasks, he liked buying and selling and business transactions the least. He did not keep books. He would have thought you had funny outlandish ideas if you had asked him what his farm plan was.

"Yet he had a plan, although it was never clearly expressed, let alone being written down. It was to produce everything possible on the farm to supply directly the family's needs, to reduce all need for things the farm could not produce, and to grow enough extra to be sold to pay for the few things that had to be bought."

In that statement is the philosophy of all the generations of farmers before our highly developed industrial society came into being; before modern commercial agriculture, with its production primarily for sale, set the stage for the rapid growth of cities; before the extension and improvements of transportation systems opened the new urban markets to commercial-minded farmers; and before the specialization in production which has accompanied the development of mechanized, scientific farming.

The old agricultural system was one in which costs and prices were of minor significance. Production costs had little meaning so long as they were all fixed costs and the produce was used at home. Selling prices are of no concern to those who do not sell. To the degree that it was a self-contained, live-at-home system of farming, it was shockproof against economic uncertainty. Outside influences touched it lightly. Whether the world on its uneven economic course should be boom-happy or depression-blue made little difference under that system.

This seeming agricultural Utopia has led some persons to advocate restoring that model of economic stability both to personal lives and to the nation. They argue that we should turn our backs on the commercial scramble and return to the self-contained farm unit.[2] As Johnstone points out, so many of us are so sensitive to the security and harmony of such a life that no counsel is more appealing than the advice to pick up where grandfather left off. But here are Johnstone's cogent reasons why a majority cannot.

[2] Elmer T. Peterson, *Forward to the Land* (Norman, University of Oklahoma Press, 1942); Elmer T. Peterson, ed., *Cities Are Abnormal* (Norman, University of Oklahoma Press, 1946).

"We cannot go back to that kind of farm life and security unless we break almost every tie with all the world that lives beyond the bend in the road. . . .

"We cannot go back to that kind of farm life and security unless we first give up automobiles and trucks and tractors and telephones and radios and electricity and every other mechanical advantage that modern science and technology have created for us. For all such things are the products of specialization and of mass-production industry that can exist only if there is beside it a specialized and commercial agriculture to feed and clothe it and supply certain raw materials. And both commercialization and specialization inevitably mean dependence on others, upon the market. . . .

"We cannot have that kind of subsistence security on the farm so long as only one in four of our total population lives on the farm, or so long as we have 131,000,000 people, for there isn't enough land suitable for widely diversified production to enable so many to make their living that way. . . .

"Grandfather bought his farm originally, at least so family tradition has it, for $1.25 an acre. The house and the other buildings on the place were constructed, a little at a time, largely by his own labor, and at least in part with materials off his own land. He never had to go into debt. He never had to lay out much cash. When he first drove west from Ohio, all of his original capital was in his pocket or in his wagon.

"Suppose the same young man were starting out from Ohio today with a team, a wagon, a plow, a few tools, a cow, and $200 in his pocket—where would he find a rich quarter section of Iowa land for $1.25 an acre? He'd have to lay out about $100 an acre, which is $16,000. . . .

"If, however, a young man who wants to establish himself on such a farm could induce some capitalist to lend him enough to buy the farm, and then to equip and stock it well enough to have any chance to pay out, he would be loaded at the very beginning with a debt of at least $20,000, which he would have to pay back with interest.

"By the very best terms he could ordinarily hope to get, he would have to lay out in cash at least $1,500 annually on amortization, interest charges, taxes, and necessary insurance and upkeep.

And to whatever extent he wanted or felt he needed a telephone, electricity, an auto or tractor or truck, and all the things that go with them, to whatever extent he wanted to see a movie, or attend the state fair, or improve his crop yields with better seed, he would increase his need for ready cash—cash on the barrel head."[3]

An operator such as the one described by Johnstone, and that means almost every young man who starts farming with the expectation of producing a good living from the land, will need cash to a degree that past generations of farmers never conceived. Commercial farming is necessary to get it—and an equal necessity is shrewd business management of the farm.[4]

Unlike grandfather's "produce it and eat it" system, commercial farming is a serious business proposition. There is no alternative if its high cash costs are to be paid and the farm family is to be provided with the comforts of modern living. Commercial-farm management, at least in the academic use of the term, has come to mean business management applied to farming.[5]

[3] "Grass Roots and Far Horizons," *Land Policy Review*, December, 1940, 6–8.

[4] It was the emergence of problems such as Johnstone describes that in the first decade after 1900 turned men like W. J. Spillman, Andrew Boss, and G. F. Warren to the study of farm management, and resulted in the establishment of the Office of Farm Management in the United States Department of Agriculture in 1905. It may be a question whether important new ideas are the product of men or of their time. In any case, however, it has been the struggle of farmers with new and complex questions involved in the business management of commercial farms that has brought farm management as a subject of investigation and teaching into every land-grant college in the country in recent years.

[5] This statement may be questioned by those who have seen businessmen turn to farming with the announced intention of "bringing business principles" to agriculture, only to come a cropper. The trouble usually is not that business principles won't work but that they are confused with farming practices. An apparent likeness between a farm practice and a business principle only too often is more apparent than real. When the businessman knows farming as well as he knows his own business, then, indeed, he can put his business knowledge to great advantage on the farm.

From the files of one of the authors comes an illustration. The businessman client insisted upon buying his farm machinery where he could "make a deal" or wangle a special price because of his business connections. Certainly the equipment-inventory sheet showed up well compared to inventories of the neighbors; but the repairs and maintenance account was tragic. The neighbors did not buy on a price basis so much as on a service basis. Most of the equipment the businessman bought could be serviced only from a city eighty-five miles away, there being no near-by dealers who handled his line of tools.

It is this background against which we propose to discuss farm organization. At the same time, however, it is well to recognize that a strictly business definition of farm management cannot be followed literally. In addition to deciding whether to grow feed crops or cash crops, whether to keep dairy cows or beef cows or neither, whether to specialize or diversify, and making a host of other "business" decisions, the manager will be equally concerned with his soil and crop management (agronomy), livestock management (animal husbandry), and an endless list of additional production problems that influence both the quantity and the quality of his produce.[6]

The broadness of the actual manager's responsibilities has been well stated by Robert R. Hudelson to include the control of production hazards, which by any strict interpretation can hardly be called business management. "Production hazards are of many kinds," says Hudelson. "They surround every plant from the time it starts in the seed and every young animal from the time it is born or even before. For practical purposes it may be said that every healthy seedling and every healthy newborn animal has in it the capacity to grow to a certain maximum size or to produce a certain maximum product if all its needs are supplied and if no handicaps are encountered. One important obligation of the farm manager is to supply as many of these needs and to remove as many of these handicaps as it is practicable and profitable for him to do."[7] It bears repeating (and this is the third time it has been

[6] Farm management, in its development as an academic subject, has quite naturally hedged itself about with the usual "academic fences." This means that the management specialists have courteously avoided encroachment upon the specialties of other scientists. Academically it might be considered the province of the farm-management man to decide whether or not poultry should be included in the organization of a certain farm; or it would be his business to analyze the results of an established poultry enterprise to determine its strengths or weaknesses. Beyond that, it would be strictly the function of a poultry-husbandry specialist to prescribe for the care, feeding, and management of the birds.

This "division of labor" has unhappily grown up in academic circles with the rapid increase in scientific knowledge. No doubt it is all proper and excellent for campus relations and the care and maintenance of academic fences, but the farmer cannot be bothered with such subdivisions of knowledge. He must manage his land and crops and animals as assiduously as he does his more strictly business affairs—all of which is to say that the successful farmer must have a working knowledge of the separate fields covered by a dozen professors.

[7] Farm Management (copyright 1939 by The Macmillan Company, New York, and used with their permission), 183.

stated in this book) that the successful business management of the farm is inseparable from sound practice in soil maintenance and crop and livestock production. Only a seventh son of a seventh son could otherwise pull a continuous year-to-year profit from between the pincers of production costs and the market price.

Brushing many complexities aside, the business of farming can be stated as a simple but fundamental equation:

$$Price - Cost = Profit\ Margin.$$

Dollars are handled to squeeze out nickels and pennies. But it is useful, even though obvious, to set out the profit as arising from operation as a unit cost that is less than the unit price.

No amount of manipulation will provide more than two ways of increasing profit margins from within the framework of this equation: One is to sell produce at favorable (meaning higher) prices; the other is to cut production costs. An axiom of commercial agriculture is that the individual farmer can find his greater profit opportunity in cost reduction rather than in price increase, for the individual can do little or nothing about prices on a bulk market.

Most farm products are staples, sold in a bulk market on a non-contract basis where the price is determined by the self-enforcing law of supply and demand. At some future date price research may provide accurate long-time market forecasts by which a farmer may direct his operations. Even in that happy day, however, he will adjust his affairs to the market, not the market to his personal wishes. Wherever farmers get together, prices and price outlook are the subject of endless discussion; and understandably so, because prices have the same meaning to the farmer as wages and hours to the industrial worker. But so far as the individual farmer has any influence upon price levels, the discussion is mostly impotent talk.

While the theory and practice of pricing might be elaborated at length, suffice it that few persons will wittingly accept a lower price or pay a higher price than is necessary to sell or to buy. Thus a free market price is always a compromise, between sellers and buyers, that balances current offerings against current demands. Neither of these can the individual farmer influence appreciably. The majority of farmers get approximately a uniform price for the same kind and quality of produce sold at the same time in the same market. True as this is, commercial farming is still the most competitive of all businesses, because the competition is on the side of production costs.

For illustration, here is the experience of thirty-three New York poultrymen who kept detailed cost accounts of their operations in 1944. The average cost to this group of farmers for producing a dozen eggs was 37.8 cents, but, significantly, not one of the thirty-three had this average cost. Their individual costs ranged from a low of 26.3 cents to a high of 74.1 cents, and among the thirty-three farmers there were thirty-two different cost figures (two had the same cost). Each producer had his own margin between the price and the cost of a dozen eggs, a margin determined largely by whether the cost was low or high. For some it was a margin of loss rather than a margin of profit.

No matter whether it is egg production in New York or California, milk in Wisconsin, cotton in the Delta, or apples in Wenatchee, there will be about as many cost figures for each product in each area as there are producers of the product. Providing always that quality is comparable, it follows that the low-cost producer is in position to net the most satisfactory margin of profit.

A top example is furnished from the operations of one of the poultrymen included in the cost-account group referred to above. Over a six-year period for which comparable data are available, he has done an outstanding job of low-cost egg production:

Comparison of Hen Account on Farm 345
with 36 Cost-account Poultrymen, 1939–1944

	Six year averages	
	36 cost-account poultrymen	Farm 345
Production per hen, eggs	163	197
Labor per 100 hens, hours	169	136
Production per hour of labor, eggs	96	145
Mortality in the laying flock, per cent	27	14
Feed cost per hen	$ 2.31	$ 2.50
Feed cost per dozen eggs	0.17	0.15
Cost of producing a dozen eggs	0.30	0.23
Price received for a dozen eggs	0.36	0.37
Labor returns per 100 hens	131.00	295.00
Labor returns per hour of labor	0.80	2.31

Annual production per hen on this farm has been maintained at an unusually high level, and at the same time flock mortality has been low. Right in line with Hudelson's concept, this operator has been exceptionally effective in controlling production hazards and in realizing to an unusual degree the potential production capacity of his hens.

What turned out to be an important contribution to his low-cost production started a few years ago in an attempt to increase his average price for poultry and eggs. The location of the farm adjacent to a large nonfarm population led the farmer to the conclusion that he could make a profit from peddling eggs and chickens at retail prices. In his bookkeeping he set up a marketing account to which all retailed produce was charged at wholesale prices. The marketing account then showed the results of his peddling operations, and his production records were left comparable with those of the other cost-accounting poultrymen who sell their products entirely at wholesale.

In order to have fowls to sell on the retail route, he culls his flocks weekly. Any hen that is not laying, and that does not look as though she soon will lay, loses her head and feathers and becomes someone's chicken dinner. This constant culling reduces mortality losses, contributes to a high rate of egg production, and, by eliminating the boarding hens, increases the efficiency of every dollar spent for feed. Note particularly that these savings in cost, added to labor-saving arrangements in his poultry houses, have been seven times as important to this farmer as has a one-cent-per-dozen price advantage. He has paid somewhat more (per hour and per ton) for both labor and feed than the other poultrymen who have kept similar records, but he has managed these cost factors with unusual efficiency and profit. Careful study of his records and first-hand observations at the farm indicate that the primary contributor to this poultryman's success has been nothing more complicated than the well-worn catching hook with which he removes the hens that do not produce. Moreover, it was not his price preference but his cost control that made profits.

It is little savings in labor, feed, mortality, and so on, that count up to big totals. One cent a dozen, or 15 cents per hen per year, is $150 on 1,000 hens—a worthwhile figure when a penny saved is a penny profit. Seven cents a dozen, as on this one farm, has meant an extra profit over competitors of $1.15 per hen per year. On 2,500 hens it has meant an additional yearly income of $2,875.

Certainly the recent war years have been an unusually favorable time to be farming. Profit margins have widened, as they always have when prices rise rapidly. But in more normal times about the only way to squeeze a profit out of average market prices is to produce at less than average cost. Below are dairy-farm figures to illustrate the point.

Production Cost, Market Price, and Profit
for 100 Pounds of Milk
New York Cost-account Farms, 1914–1943

	Per hundredweight of milk			Earnings per hour of labor on dairy cows
PERIOD	COST	PRICE	PROFIT	
1914–18	$2.20	$2.15	$–0.05	$0.30
1919–23	2.82	2.54	–0.28	0.25
1924–28	2.66	2.63	–0.03	0.40
1929–33	2.50	2.09	–0.41	0.14
1934–38	1.96	1.89	–0.07	0.25
1939–43	2.24	2.53	0.09	0.55
1914–43	$2.40	$2.31	$–0.09	$0.32

The dairymen who have kept these records on their operations have co-operated with the College of Agriculture at Cornell in studies of the cost of producing farm products. They have not been selected on any basis except their willingness and ability to keep complete and accurate account books; that is, no attempt has been made to include only the better operators in these studies. Nevertheless, in practice it has been found that farmers who keep detailed accounts are in fact superior operators. These cost-account dairymen have better than average cows, do a better than average job of feeding, get better than average milk yields, and are better than average managers. Yet, over the past thirty years, they have failed by nine cents a hundredweight to break even on their milk-producing operations.

In the accounting procedures by which these figures were determined, all labor, including that of the farm operator, was charged as a cost. The average cost of dairy-farm labor over the thirty years was thirty-six cents an hour, but the cows did not return that much. After paying all other costs except labor, the cows returned only thirty-two cents an hour for the time expended on them. Thus if the average of these dairymen hired half of the labor used on his herd, the hired man got thirty-six cents an hour (four cents more than the cows paid), and the operator got twenty-eight cents (eight cents less than the hired man).

Yet, there were individual farmers in this group of dairymen who over the years have so managed their herds as to make double the average return to labor, who have hired labor successfully and made a profit on the hired man above his wages. They have been the low-cost producers.

A generation of farm-management research has evolved "certain principles that must be observed in the organization and operation of a farm if it is to be financially successful."[8] These yardsticks of successful farming deal with the efficient utilization of labor, land, livestock, equipment, supplies, and other cost factors of production—that is, they are management principles which are applied to the farm business with the objective of reducing production costs.

The measures of success listed have varied considerably in different works on farm management, but among the more important ones are the following:

1. *Efficient use of the farm labor force.* The more effectively the combination of labor and equipment on a particular farm may be used—in terms of yearly production per man—the lower the unit cost of production may be. (See Chapter 15.) Higher output per dollar spent on labor and equipment spreads these overhead costs across more units of product, thus reducing the cost of each unit.

2. *Rate of production per acre and per animal.* High-yielding crops and high-producing livestock require little more labor than low producers. Likewise, in terms of cost per bushel or per ton,

8 H. C. M. Case, R. H. Wilcox, and H. A. Berg, *Organizing the Corn Belt Farm for Profitable Production* (Illinois Agricultural Experiment Station Bulletin 329, Revised, 1934), 262.

they make more profitable use of land, buildings, and machinery. If they are not obtained at disproportionate expenditures for fertilizer and feed, high rates of production from the acres and animals on the farm are prime factors in cost cutting. (See Chapter 25.)

3. *Balanced combination of crops and livestock.* Of course, the proper balance varies for each farm and each farmer. But crop and livestock enterprises carefully fitted together may provide for optimum soil maintenance, may reduce cash costs and increase cash income, may provide for optimum utilization of labor and equipment over the year, and still spread other items of fixed overhead so that the unit costs of production are reduced. (See Chapter 24.)

4. *Size of the farm business.* The size of the farm operation may have two major influences upon profits. The first arises from the fact that certain expenses do not vary directly with farm size. For example, the purchase price of a tractor and the fixed overhead for its maintenance is much the same, whether used 200 hours or 600 hours a year. As maximum use is approximated, the hourly costs of tractor operation decrease notably. The same influences prevail with all fixed and partially fixed overhead costs, up to the point where full use is made of these contributors to production.

The other influence of size is that it functions as a multiplier. This means simply that if a farmer can operate successfully enough to have a margin of profit on each bushel or hundredweight produced, he may multiply his profits by getting greater volume.

Of course, size cuts both ways, because it can multiply losses as well; but where size increases are wisely made to a farm that is well managed, they normally function as a profit booster. (See Chapter 18.)

Most certainly, the objective of farm management may be more easily stated than attained. Were that not so, farming would be a more crowded field than it now is. Since the farmer has more control over his unit costs than he has over his prices, there is but one concise summary of his complex function as a manager; that is to work aggressively and continuously toward lowering costs. The politicians and the consumer will set prices after their own peculiar humor.

24. What Crops? Which Livestock?

IN *The Cherokee Strip*[1] Marquis James tells of the tobacco crop that was to have built an addition to his boyhood home near Enid, Oklahoma. It turned out to be a no-profit crop. Sugar cane was tried next but did no better. The house remained "a two-story dwelling without a stairway." Experiences such as these were a part of the trial-and-error farming that featured the early years after The Strip was opened to settlement. Moreover, they were but a repetition of the necessary shakedown period through which, in its turn, every new agricultural area in the country has gone.

Into all parts of the frontier, settlers took the livestock and every crop they had produced in the widely divergent areas whence they came. Then began the great experiment. What part of that varying past experience was good and could be continued? What part had to be discarded because it did not fit the new environment?

In the eighteen seventies a group of Mennonite immigrants from the Russian Crimea brought Turkey-red wheat to the plains of central Kansas. In this strain they had a crop so peculiarly adapted to its new home that it has since expanded to cover millions of acres. It has extended into The Strip where the James family found that merely being in the "latitude of North Carolina, the finest tobacco country in the world" was not enough to insure success with their tobacco. In contrast to this triumph of a Russian wheat were the orchards and vineyards planted by Jules Sandoz in the upper Niobrara country of western Nebraska.[2] Those plantings were no more successful than the James's tobacco and sugar cane—although they were in the latitude of the lush horticultural areas around the lower Great Lakes. More than latitude is involved in the determination of climatic and soil variations.

Basic to the problem of farm organization is the question of which crops will thrive best under the local conditions. Then, what livestock (if any) will best utilize the crops produced. Commercial farmers must be guided by both the natural environment and the economic environment within which their individual farms must be operated.

[1] (New York, The Viking Press, 1946), 17.
[2] Mari Sandoz, *Old Jules* (Boston, Little, Brown, and Company, 1935).

182

In organizing a farm today, the operator finds many guide-posts the pioneers did not have. Old Jules, the Jameses, and the other families who have gone before have made many of the possible mistakes. From what each locality has continued to produce, the newcomer will find his directions. Present farming systems may not be the best possible, for conditions are ever changing. But where the major crop is corn, or cotton, or wheat, or fruit, or pasture, there is a compelling reason. The experience back of that reason should not be treated lightly.

In the science of biology there is a concept stated as the law of limiting and optimum environment.[3] It deals with the fact (obvious, perhaps, though certainly fundamental) that either too much or too little of any influence such as light, temperature, moisture, soil acidity, and so on will be adverse to plant growth. That, in essence, is the law of limits. For example, if a plant receives no water, it dies, because water is essential in its life processes. If it receives too much water, it drowns, because the oxygen supply to its roots is shut off. Temperature may impose similar limits —so likewise may each of the other essential conditions for growth. Furthermore, each condition acts independently. Should light, temperature, soil, and all other conditions except moisture be highly favorable to a certain crop, the lack of moisture alone would still veto a proposal to grow it unless irrigation could be developed.[4]

Fortunately, however, different plants vary in their tolerance to environment. A growing season too short for cotton may still be ideal for highly productive types of corn (Illinois *vs.* the Mississippi Delta). Too little moisture for corn may yet be adequate for wheat or sorghum (Kansas *vs.* Iowa). A growing season too cool for best results with tomatoes and corn may be highly favorable

---

[3] See K. H. W. Klages, *Ecological Crop Geography* (New York, The Macmillan Company, 1942), 106; and Huntington, Williams, and van Valkenburg, *Economic and Social Geography* (New York, John Wiley and Sons, 1933), 52.

[4] This is just a restatement of the law of the minimum expressed more than a hundred years ago by Justus von Liebig: "The yield of any crop always depends on that nutrient constituent which is present in the minimum amount." In his statement Liebig was dealing with the plant nutrients in the soil; but obviously the principle may be expanded to cover all factors of the natural environment.

for potatoes, oats, and grass (Maine *vs.* Indiana). Only by trial and error did the early settlers of any region find the necessary adjustment for their own conditions.

Yet adjustment to the law of limits, which may have been all right for grandfather, is not enough in today's commercial farming. In the competitive business of balancing cash receipts against cash costs, the law of the optimum has pushed to the fore. This principle of biology recognizes that somewhere between the upper and lower extremes within which a crop may be grown there is a certain intermediate point at which growth will be most favorable, where yields will be most profitable, and where the opportunity for high-volume, low-cost production will be most enhanced. To the degree that one grows crops under conditions much removed from the optimum, he invites lower yields and higher costs, thus complicating his job as a manager. The self-sufficing farmer, whether he be out on a frontier beyond the lines of transportation (self-sufficiency imposed by location) or demonstrating his independence on a suburban residential farm (self-sufficiency self-imposed), will grow potatoes if he wants potatoes, so long as the law of limits imposes no barrier. If his yield is only fifty bushels an acre, he would still grow potatoes, simply because the objective of his farming would be to raise everything possible to supply his family's needs with no consideration of the labor cost.

We heard a Northeastern farmer ask a visiting relative why he did not have a vegetable plot and an orchard on his Dakota wheat farm. "Oh, it would be just a dirty spot on the farm," was the reply. "And we couldn't do the fussing for the little bit we would get from it." Not all Dakota farmers would or do feel the same way. But the principal point this grower was making is that the climate of his community is more favorable (or less unfavorable) for the wheat, barley, and range cattle that he raises than for vegetables and fruit trees. It was recognition that economics (adjustment to the optimum) imposes more narrow limits upon commercial farming than biology; and that one principle of commercial-farm organization is to select the most promising enterprises for which the particular farm offers the nearest approach to a biological optimum.

Yet, natural environment is only one reason for selecting the specific crop and livestock enterprises for any given farm. Another, and to the commercial farmer equally important consideration, is economic environment.

In a previous chapter we have emphasized the difficulty faced by an individual farmer in getting consistently higher prices than his neighbors, unless through unusual control of the production hazards he is able to produce consistently higher quality. While this is true within any one neighborhood, it is not true between different sections of the country. Producers but a few miles removed from their consumers receive a higher price, net at the farm, than do more distant growers for the same item sold in the same market at the same time. The reason is simple: Transportation costs are less. Such a neighborhood and the farmers within it thus have an advantage of location. It is an economic advantage, a net-price advantage, which may be used in whole or in part to offset some production disadvantage. It may permit fortunately located farmers to raise a crop under soil and climatic conditions less favorable than more distant farmers would be able to use.

For a simplified illustration of the location factor (relative market advantage), suppose a farmer starts for market with one hundred bushels of corn on a wagon. On the way he feeds some of his load to his team and trades some more for meals and shelter. When he has reached his destination, he has used ten bushels in this manner. He sells eighty bushels and retains the other ten to pay his way home. Having been able to sell only eighty bushels out of one hundred, his corn is worth 80 per cent as much at the farm as at the market—the marketing costs literally ate up the other 20 per cent.

Suppose another farmer, more distantly located, has to use forty bushels out of each one hundred to get to market and back. His location is obviously less favorable. He might decide that he gets so little net out of each one hundred bushels gross that he cannot afford to raise corn under those conditions. If, however, he has more nearly optimum climate and soil for corn than his competitor, he may get a yield that would offset his marketing disadvantage. The Corn Belt *vs.* the rest of the country is an example.

If these two growers were in competition on a seasonal and perishable product instead of corn, the one more distant might find it possible to mature and market his crop when near-by production would be off the market. He might then get an out-of-season price that would give him the sought-for margin of profit. This is the case of the Florida or South Texas *vs.* the New Jersey vegetable grower.

Failing this, the distant producer might change his type of farming to reduce his marketing disadvantage. Should he feed his corn to livestock, he could concentrate from six to ten pounds of grain into one pound of meat. Or he might produce milk which could then be concentrated ten to one into cheese or twenty to one into butter. With products of this type his marketing handicap would be less. Each pound, having a greater value than a pound of corn, would buy more feed, food, and lodging on the trip to market, and marketing costs would be a correspondingly smaller part of the load with which the farmer started. This is the reason Nebraska poultry is strongly competitive to Northeastern supplies on the New York market.

Precisely in the manner illustrated, marketing opportunities and costs may influence commercial-farm organization, the crop and livestock enterprises selected, and the form in which produce is marketed. It makes no difference whether the marketing expenses are paid with a part of the load or whether the produce is delivered to a railroad and the expenses paid in cash. The principle is the same. Location is seen to be an economic factor, an influence of economic environment quite apart from the natural environment factors of climate and soil.

In commercial farming it is axiomatic that the individual farm unit shall be adjusted to its own combination of production and marketing opportunities. Neither one may be considered in isolation from the other. The objective is to maximize the advantages and minimize the disadvantages. A handicap in either production or marketing may not eliminate any one crop or livestock if a sufficient advantage in the other direction can be utilized to offset it.

Whatever farming region has a cost advantage in producing a certain product will be found to have favorable climate or soil—the real factor being the law of the optimum. (Wisconsin dairying and Iowa corn are top examples.) Similarly, a regional advantage in selling will be explained by the law of location.[5] (New Jersey eggs and Long Island vegetables are instances.) A farmer of our acquaintance on the Lake Erie plain has furnished an excellent example of how the influences may work on an individual farm. "When I came here about thirty years ago," he said, "we started growing an acre or two of potatoes each year. The reason was to have potatoes for our own use, but we always had a few to sell over in the village. They sold well, so we increased to about five acres, and continued to raise them for a good many years. But recently those fellows on the mucklands down below here have greatly expanded their potato acreage, and they can get about three times the yield I can. They can make money at prices at which I would go broke. They have a production advantage that I can't over-come, so I've quit growing potatoes, raise more alfalfa, and keep some more cows." Then he added, "Come out to the tool shed; I'll sell you a planter and digger cheap."

He had adjusted his farm organization to his comparative advantage in producing milk and potatoes. Potatoes had lost out in spite of his favorable market because he could not produce cheaply enough. The point in his thinking that needs emphasis is that he had an alternative. It is a basic but much misunderstood fact that farmers select their enterprises entirely in terms of their own alternatives, not on the basis of whether they or other farmers can produce a product more cheaply.

Consider, for example, the case of a dairy farmer who is oper-ating on land so close to the margin in quality that it could hardly be used for dairying at a reasonable profit even under top-quality management. Other dairymen on land that will produce pasture and hay far superior to that which he can grow will be able to pro-duce milk at less cost per hundredweight. Yet he continues to be a dairyman if he has no alternative in a type of farming that would be more profitable. His income may be low and may be reflected in his standard of living, but without a higher-profit alternative, he still would be operating in full accord with the principle of maximum comparative advantage if he continued as a dairyman. In similar circumstances the situation would be identical regard-less of the type of farming.

5 The combination of these locational and natural environmental influ-ences has been back of what Robert West Howard has called "the birth of the belts" (i.e., the Corn Belt, the Dairy Belt, the Wheat Belt, and other regions of specialization). See Howard's *Two Billion Acre Farm* (New York, Doubleday, Doran, and Company, 1945), 69.

To specialize or to diversify? Here is yet another controversy raging perennially across the farm front. Much of the common thinking on this question, as on so many others, has been conditioned by history. Even those of us whose forebears followed Greelcy's advice to "Go West" have roots somewhere back East. And the East has been a region of great diversity in farming. From three to a half-dozen grain crops, at least as many more food crops grown in field quantities and supplemented by all the diverse vegetables the garden would hold, a variety of fruits limited only by climate, cattle and sheep and hogs, and all the poultry that quacked, hissed, gobbled, or cackled! This was the Down-East assortment that grandfather produced in his live-at-home plan of farming. It was the heritage of much of the country until the time of World War I. Even today, it is still the model cited by some persons as a secure pattern for an idealistic farm; but commercial farmers thinking less of the alleged spiritual value and more of paying the mortgage have drifted and are drifting steadily away from it.

It is not that diversity lacks appeal if conditions permit. With diverse crops one balances the demands upon his land, his labor force, and his equipment. He balances his risk. He is much less the pawn of chance. He is not prince, then pauper. His coefficient of independence is increased. Surely, diversity has great advantages—unless it costs too much.

Some commercial farmers are so favorably situated with respect to markets, soils, and climate that a wide diversity of enterprises is open to their choosing. They are usually diversified producers. When alternative enterprises are about equally promising, the risks of specialization may quickly tarnish the appeal to specialize. There remains, however, a large and growing number of producers who find their alternatives more limited.

The law of the optimum pushes ever harder as high-volume, low-cost production becomes increasingly the difference between a "living" and a successful farm business. The vast growth of science and mechanics applied to farming is fostering specialization. The rising productivity of labor, not only in agriculture, but even more so in industry, is boosting the product-cost of labor, making necessary an ever increasing quantity of production per man from which current wage rates can be paid. If this rising wage trend is not met with corresponding boosts in labor productivity on the farm, the operator dips into his own earnings to pay the hired man (see Chapter 17). Though the farm may be operated without hired help, the family's living standard still fails to rise to the average standard of other American families. Specialization in production pervades the whole American economic system and is basic to the world-renowned American standard of living. The commercial farmer (or business farmer, or cash farmer—call him what you will) is merely joining the trend and participating in the established pattern.

On few farms and in few areas is there any considerable diversity of enterprises that, considering both the production opportunities of the farm and the marketing opportunities of the region, will pay equally well for the costs incurred in production. This is the primary reason for specialization. Certainly, the specializing farmer can, and does, go broke most quickly in bad times. His risks of crop failure and of price failure are increased. The larger his cash outgo the less able he will be to "farm at a loss year after year and still get by." But specialization dictated by the law of the optimum and the law of location is an attempt to farm at a profit instead of at a loss. It is the intelligent adjustment for the producer who does have near-optimum conditions and a favorable market for a profitable specialty. It is likewise the quick way to ruin on those less fortunate farm units where the supposed advantage of any specialty is more fancy than fact. Just as there are high-cost copper mines and high-cost steel mills, so there are high-cost farms even with the best of management. Such farms, and they comprise a large group indeed, had best be farmed by grandfather's Down-East pattern of diversity while commercial specialization should be held at a minimum.

Thus the answer to the specialize-or-diversify problem appears to be not one but two. There should be both types, as there now are. When the risks are considered on a year-to-year basis, specialization introduces additional hazard into farming—a business already characterized by hazard. This is true simply because of dependence upon the specialty. If over a period of years, however, specialization promises significantly higher average yearly income, even the most diversity-conscious minister of security would find it difficult to argue that the specialization is not justified. He would be reduced to questioning what is a significantly higher income. That question must be resolved for each farm individually and must be recognized, moreover, as basic to the whole problem of organizing the farm.

D. Howard Doane points out that the memory of farmers does not run back to the time when they have not been advised to diversify. "In the wheat belt the common council of self appointed advisers has been, 'The only way to make this a good country is to diversify.' 'The trouble with the corn belt is too much corn.' 'The only thing that will save the cotton belt is to grow less cotton, and more of other crops.'

"If I were to express my opinion on this subject after a fairly wide experience in actually producing these crops in their respective belts, I would say, 'The thing that will surely break the wheat, corn, or cotton belts is to grow too small amounts of the crops best adapted to them.' . . .

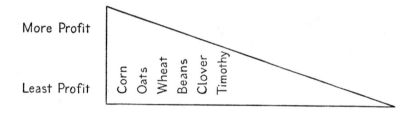

"Let us diagram our situation. We will make a triangle. At the left we will indicate the dominant crop of the region, in this case, corn. At the right we will show the other crops which we may grow in obtaining diversification. It will be noted that as we pass from corn, to oats, to wheat, to soybeans, and the other crops that the line of profit goes steadily down. (There has been no attempt to arrange the crops in the exact order of actual profit.) Of course, this is as we would anticipate. There is always a most profitable and a least profitable crop in each region. Thus, as we extend diversification we decrease the margin of profit if not lose it entirely on those added crops. The farther we go the worse it gets. The more low or no-profit crops we grow the greater the shrink in our income. In short, the more completely we follow the advice of the crop diversificationists the worse off we are financially."[6]

Specialization, on the other hand, does not usually mean one crop. Rather, it means giving the dominant place in the use of land and in the order of work to the most profitable enterprise. It means that the maximum amount of the highest-profit alternative shall be grown that is consistent with good rotation practice, soil maintenance, weed control, disease control, available labor, market opportunity, and justifiable risk. Then, and only then, every other crop or livestock that may contribute significantly to the success of the farm as a whole is chinked around the main enterprise. The very concept of "chinking" is good because it implies filling up the holes without interfering with the main line of production.

A farmer may raise a half-dozen crops and livestock and yet concentrate his attention on only one or two. His other enterprises would be considered supplementary to his specialty if they used labor and equipment at off seasons and occupied a place in the crop rotation that did not interfere with his major profit item. A few acres of cabbage on a Wisconsin dairy farm is a good illustration of a supplementary crop. Others are the five- or six-cow dairy herds that are kept on many Corn Belt farms, or the small poultry flocks so common in all sections, or even oats in the Central and Eastern states.

Cost studies have repeatedly shown oats to be a low-profit crop (often a no-profit crop) in both the Corn Belt and the dairy regions. This fact does not necessarily mean that oats should be eliminated. It means: Select a more profitable main enterprise but continue the oats as a chinker if nothing better can be found. On many farms, oats occupy a place in the rotation that is otherwise difficult to fill. They come between corn and hay, and are grown as a companion crop with the new hay seeding. Even though they fail to pay all costs in full, they help to carry some overhead. They provide useful straw and feed at small cash outlay. At their place in the rotation they do not compete for land. Since they are planted and harvested when other crops are not pressing, they seldom compete for labor. By the strictest accounting, the farm as a whole may be more successful because they are grown. Failing to find a more

[6] "Perpendicular Diversification," *Journal of the American Society of Farm Managers and Rural Appraisers,* April, 1938, 20–21.

profitable substitute, the proper management adjustment would be to get the best variety for the locality, high-quality seed of that variety, and do a good job of raising oats.

Another illustration of chinking is the practice of a successful dairyman of our acquaintance who added a potato enterprise to his specialized dairy farm. He had a peak load of work each morning and evening at milking time. Additional crop work in summer plus sorting and hauling in the winter helped to even out these labor peaks. He now grows eighteen acres of potatoes each year with no extra help except at harvest.

Some fruit farms are evidence that there may be diversity within specialization. About fifteen years ago in the southwestern corner of Michigan a young man took over a farm where forty acres of apples were the major enterprise. He set additional orchards to bring the rest of his cropland into fruit. His new plantings included twelve acres of peaches, six acres of cherries, and ten acres of pears. He now raises nothing but fruit, but he has four kinds of fruit instead of one. They require spraying, thinning, and harvesting at different times. Peach thinning comes in June, cherry harvest in early July. Apple thinning follows. Peaches are harvested in late August and early September. Pear harvest follows the peaches, and apple picking extends into October. This diversity spreads labor needs more uniformly over the season and reduces the great labor peaks that result from all acreage being in one fruit. Similarly, the diversity permits more efficient use of the fruit-growing equipment. And, of course, it reduces the risk.

Last, here is an illustration of enterprise selection by a young man who reorganized a farm and doubled its net income. In the late nineteen thirties he bought out an elderly owner-operator, getting 120 acres of highly productive cropland that had been used in a six-year rotation of corn for grain, field beans, oats, wheat, clover, and timothy. Twenty-six acres of pasture, plus sheep pens and a small dairy stable in the barn basement, had been used for one hundred ewes and eight cows.

On other farms in the community he found various combinations of the same enterprises. In addition, alfalfa and corn silage were common feed crops. Widely grown cash crops were cabbage and canning-factory vegetables (including sweet corn, snap beans, peas, beets, and tomatoes). Many of his neighbors kept dairy cows and hens. Others were livestock feeders. Some of these fed lambs or steers, and some bought dairy heifers off pasture in the fall and sold them as close springers and fresh cows in the spring. It was a community of diversified general farming. All of these enterprises the newcomer looked upon as alternatives among which he might choose. Since he had a young family and a mortgage, income was his necessary objective.

Two years of experience on the farm and much checking with his county agent and successful farmer neighbors resulted in establishing the following rotation: field corn (half for grain and half for silage), twenty acres; cabbage, twenty acres; canning-factory sweet corn, twenty acres; wheat (seeded to hay), twenty acres; and alfalfa mixed hay (left down two years), forty acres.

His hay seeding mixture is alfalfa, ladino clover, and timothy. This was chosen over red clover and timothy because on his land it will produce greater yield, more profit, and better feed. It is left down two years to get economy of seeding cost, maximum soil-building value, and the amount of forage required for his livestock. Likewise, wheat was chosen over oats because under his conditions it will produce more net value per acre if it is sold or more feed per acre if it is used on the farm.

His row-cropping program was extended to three years out of six instead of the former two out of six. This was done to substitute a higher-profit crop for oats. The row-crop sequence—field corn, cabbage, and sweet corn—required little specialized equipment, considerable use for the equipment items that were needed, a good distribution of labor over the growing and harvesting season, and satisfactory net profit per acre.

It is worthy of note here that enterprises cannot be selected on the basis of gross value per acre. The gross tells nothing at all about the net profit. Even comparative net incomes are not an entirely satisfactory basis of selection. For example, this operator tried canning-factory beets for two years. But the high labor cost and the hard work of weeding, pulling, and topping caused him to drop them. As he said, to him the net return was not worth the "work and worry." He by-passed snap beans for the same reason. In some years he has raised canning-factory tomatoes in place of part of his cabbage. They require the same equipment, but the tomato harvest demands a large amount of hand labor and conflicts with sweet-corn harvest, silo filling, and seeding wheat. It is a high-profit crop if he can get it picked. Therefore, his decision to grow tomatoes is conditioned by the outlook for harvest labor.

The livestock enterprises that accompany his revised cropping program are twenty dairy cows, eight to ten heifers, and six hundred hens. Of all the forage-consuming livestock that he might have chosen, the cows were selected because they would produce the greatest total net income. They provide much productive work in winter, which is desirable—but also considerable work in summer, which for him is less desirable. At present he needs the income. When the farm is paid for, he says, he will probably dispose of the cows and feed steers or dairy heifers in winter only.

The six hundred hens are housed in a 24x40-foot building that was converted for two floors of poultry. They are handled by a son, now fourteen years old, as his personal project.

By his careful figuring and forward planning, this young farmer has doubled the productive work that the farm provides. Yet with a fuller use of equipment and mechanical power, the labor force has increased only 40 per cent—from 2.0 to 2.8 man-equivalents. Accomplishment per man has been increased nearly 50 per cent. Net farm income, with costs and prices figured on a comparable basis, is two and a quarter times what the former owner made. This family can live better and still pay for the farm at least two or three times as fast as would have been possible had they continued the farm organization they found when they acquired the business.

Yet the present selection of crops and livestock is no definitely final answer. Market opportunities and relative prices for different products will continue to change with time. Continuous figuring of alternatives is necessary for a top-profit operation—and this farmer knows it full well.

25. Diminishing Returns—the Guiding Principle of Management

THE *Country Gentleman* for August 28, 1920, carried an article by J. Sidney Cates dealing with the response of cotton yields to fertilizer. For several years the North Carolina Department of Agriculture had been conducting fertilizer experiments on its Edgecombe Test Farm, where on unfertilized soil they were getting an acre yield of 160 pounds (0.32 of a bale) of lint cotton. Fertilizer tests started with an application of 200 pounds per acre. Other plots were treated more heavily, with successive 200-pound increments up to applications of 1,000 pounds. Yield increases were as follows:

Fertilizer application POUNDS	Yield of lint cotton per acre FRACTIONS OF A BALE
0	0.320
200	0.525
400	0.720
600	0.800
800	0.905
1,000	0.980

It was these results that Cates had observed and on the basis of which he wrote an enthusiastic article advocating increased use of fertilizer on farms. Toward growers who could get similar yield response it was an enthusiasm well directed. At price relationships then prevailing, the additional harvest far more than paid the increased cost.

Whatever influence the story may have had on farm practice, it produced another very tangible effect. W. J. Spillman, mathematician, biologist, and economist (long-time chief of the Office of Management of the United States Department of Agriculture) read the article and studied carefully the experimental results. He charted the reported increases in yield and fitted a curve to his chart. He found that each successive 200 pounds of fertilizer had returned about three-quarters as much yield increase as had the preceding 200 pounds. Next, by mathematical formula he calculated a geometrically decreasing series of numbers that proved to agree closely with the experimental yields. The two series of figures are shown below:

Fertilizer application POUNDS	Actual increase in yield* POUNDS	"Expected" increase calculated by mathematical formula POUNDS
200	102.5	103.9
400	85.0	80.0
600	62.5	61.8
800	45.0	49.4
1,000	32.5	34.9

* Actual yield as read from the curve Spillman fitted to the experimental results.

This close agreement between actual yields and his "expected" (or calculated) yields led Spillman to further study. He investigated the response of potato yields in Idaho to a varying number of six-inch applications of irrigation water. Each successive six inches added two-thirds as much yield as the preceding six inches. And again the diminishing increase in production was mathematically precise. From Professor T. L. Haecker he obtained the results of Minnesota steer-feeding experiments. As these steers increased in age and weight, they used additional feed less and less efficiently—with a diminishing rate of gain that was mathematically exact in relation to previous gains from previous feed. He reviewed feeding experiments with hogs and poultry, and also fertilizer results with corn, wheat, cotton, tobacco, potatoes, hay, and other crops in various parts of the country. Each result was similar. Successive quantities of feed or fertilizer resulted in production increases that in each case were fixed fractions of previous gains. Spillman's studies were published in 1924 in a highly significant little book, *The Law of Diminishing Returns*.[1]

The publisher's foreword to this book states: "In these days of high production costs it is essential that the agriculturist be able to make an intelligent study of his costs in their relation to his returns." It might be added that this is the significance of diminishing returns to farmers at all times. It is the vital question of net profits. Feed and fertilizer are costs; so also are land, labor, and

[1]New York, The World Book Company, 1924.

equipment. Since each of these production factors is a cost, each one has to be used economically. The challenge to the manager is how to combine them into an efficient and profitable business under his own conditions.

Your own problem as a farm manager is briefly this: What combination of land, labor, equipment, and materials, each of which costs you something, will give you maximum production at minimum outlay?

Spillman's contribution came directly from his studies stimulated by Cates' article. He interpreted the progressively decreasing yields from additional applications of production materials as a "law." He called it the "law of diminishing increment."

Applied to your animals and crops, it is a natural law. Successive units of fertilizer or water dumped upon a constant acreage will give less and less additional yield. Or, as a steer increases in weight, a smaller proportion of his total feed is converted into further gain. Or again, the first pound of grain fed to a cow will produce more milk than the last pound you give her.[2]

Since these materials are cost factors, and the second ton will cost as much as the first, the diminishing increment translates directly into an economic law of diminishing net returns. Profit is the end point. On profit the manager's attention will obviously focus when he is trying to determine how much fertilizer to use, or to what weight to feed his hogs, or how high a finish to put on his cattle.

There is no one solution to such questions. More than anything else it will be related to comparative costs of materials and prices of produce. This is one more need for pencil work in farming, and for studying economic trends. When the livestock-feed ratios are wide—that is, when feed is cheap and livestock is high, as in 1942, 1943, and 1944—heavy feeding and high finish make money. It may be an invitation to the sheriff if you feed the same way when the cost–price relationships are reversed.

When, as in recent years, crops are high and fertilizer is cheap, feed the land well. When milk overflows the market, let the cows eat grass. Grass is cheaper than grain—more so at some times than at others.

2 See Einar Jensen *et al.*, *Input-Output Relationships in Milk Production* (U.S.D.A. Technical Bulletin No. 815, May, 1942).

Corn yields in response to nitrogen fertilizer were investigated by the North Carolina Agriculture Experiment Station in 1944. A summary of the findings was published in *The Country Gentleman* for November, 1945. Again, J. Sidney Cates wrote the article.

In presenting the results of the trials, Director L. D. Baver of the Experiment Station said, "We confidently expect to double the corn yield in this state within the next decade." Following are the experimental data which prompted that prediction:

Nitrogen fertilizer used (expressed in equivalent pounds of nitrate of soda)	Corn yield (bushels per acre)
0	21
125	32
250	48
375	59
500	63
750	72

Results such as these indicate that a doubling of yield may be much more than possible providing (1) the fertilizer will be used and (2) the soils over the state will be as responsive as on the farms where these tests were made.

To study the results in greater detail, we have charted the yields and fitted a curve to the chart. The summaries are shown opposite. Data on costs and returns at the various levels of fertilizer application were furnished by Professor B. A. Krantz, who was in charge of the experimental work.

How should a manager use his fertilizer? In this test, the first 375 pounds produced a thirty-eight-bushel increase in yield; the second 375, a thirteen-bushel increase (Spillman again). Obviously, if fertilizer were hard to get and had to be "stretched," the farmer might better put his 750 pounds on two acres than on one.

In recent years fertilizer prices have stayed low while labor and land have gone up. Fertilizer is a bargain. Rather lavish use is desirable if it will increase the net returns available to more important cost factors.[3] Cheap fertilizer should be used as much as possible to boost the accomplishment of high-cost labor. Suburban farmers, truck growers, and others with very intensive crops commonly use much fertilizer to help offset their high land costs.

Summary of Corn Fertilizer Experiment
North Carolina Agricultural Experiment Station, 1944

Nitrogen fertilizer applied per acre
(pounds of nitrate of soda equivalent)

	0	125	250	375	500	625	750
Bushels per acre as read from the yield curve	21	34	48	59	65	69	72
Additional yield, bushels	—	13	14	11	6	4	3
Value of crop at $1.50 per bu.	$31.50	$51.00	$72.00	$88.50	$97.50	$103.50	$108.00
Costs per acre	31.05	35.70	40.20	44.20	47.80	50.90	53.75
Net profit	$ 0.45	$15.30	$31.80	$44.30	$49.70	$ 52.60	$ 54.25
Additional profit	—	14.85	16.50	12.50	5.40	2.90	1.65
Returns per hour of labor	$ 0.31	$ 0.65	$ 0.99	$ 1.23	$ 1.31	$ 1.35	$ 1.37
Cost per bushel of corn	$ 1.48	$ 1.05	$ 0.84	$ 0.75	$ 0.74	$ 0.74	$ 0.75

A common misconception leads to figuring the gain on the fertilizer as the gross value of the increased yield after subtracting the fertilizer cost. Not to be overlooked is that harvesting and marketing costs increase likewise when yields go up. Net profit above all costs is, of course, the true objective.

In the particular case of these North Carolina corn trials, even the last unit of fertilizer produced three bushels more yield; the next to last produced four bushels. Under the prevailing cost and price conditions these were still profitable increases, but it should be noted that the margin of increased profit was small. Either lower corn prices or dry weather might easily wipe them out. Thus the important conclusion is simply this: Risks in farming are so great (weather, pests, and prices) that a conservative grower will not go after the last bushel or two of yield which ideal conditions will produce. Each manager must determine for himself what is his justifiable risk (discretion *vs.* valor).

The problem of diminishing returns does not end with production supplies as discussed above. It extends also to land, livestock, equipment, and labor.

Brief reference to Part 1 will re-emphasize that some soils are naturally more productive than others. Likewise, some soils, though

3 See Herrell DeGraff, "Substitute and Save," *Farm Journal*, April, 1946, 28.

low in natural productivity, are highly responsive to management. Still others are both poor and unresponsive. Diminishing returns may quickly defeat any more than meager attempts to improve this last kind. Fertilizer use may be discouraged because a soil is shallow, or poorly drained, or too sandy to hold the nutrients. Irrigation may be unprofitable on porous, gravelly soils of low fertility. Intensive cultivation may be limited because the soil is heavy and hard to work. Land coming under these classifications has small capacity to absorb other cost factors used with it. Diminishing returns may bear down quickly as additional amounts of labor, equipment, fertilizer, and good seed are combined with it in production.

Next, in the case of livestock, some animals are more responsive to feed and care than others. High production and rapid gains are essential to profits, but actually to get the profit there must not be excessive cost. A dairyman acquaintance recently said: "If my checkbook would only last long enough, I could get the best bull index or cow-production record in the country. But I've got to make a living from this farm, so I can't afford to do it."

The animals with high inherent capacity are the ones that will profitably utilize high levels of feed and labor expense. Consequently, these same animals will ward off diminishing returns until a high rate of production has been achieved. This may or may not mean pedigreed stock. In the battle for profits, production is what is needed more than a piece of paper describing ancestry.[4]

It must be recognized that some equipment works more efficiently than other. Though it does more work and better work, the question always remains: Is it worth its cost on your farm? Or will diminishing returns on equipment set in before your land and livestock can absorb its cost? This problem emphasizes the necessity of fitting the equipment to the individual farm.

Nor is the farm labor force exempt from diminishing returns. Some men can do more and better work than others without the constant close supervision of the manager. Some are more capable in handling livestock and equipment. The horseman must be discriminated against who lathers up his team and excites them to nervousness by his own ineptitude; so likewise must the man who

[4] See Vernon Vine, "Are Purebreds Phony?" *Farm Journal,* December, 1945, 23.

cannot take high-speed, expensive equipment to the field and get the work done without excessive breakdowns or crop damage.

It is the men with high capacity to handle machines and animals who get high production per dollar of expense. By this very capacity to make profitable use of other cost factors, dependable, competent, intelligent help delays the point where diminishing returns begin to apply to labor.

Since diminishing returns apply to every cost factor in farming, it becomes obvious that the real solution is in management. The things the manager works with—that is, land, labor, livestock, equipment, and production supplies—are just "crazy-quilt pieces" until put together in a well-balanced pattern. There is not even a "centerpiece" around which to build, except the manager himself. If he uses five cost factors in production, he has at least that many separate points of diminishing returns with which to deal. To illustrate, there is the inevitable decrease in profits from feed if it is not balanced with the number and quality of his livestock; or from fertilizer if it is not balanced with his soil and crop; or from land if it is not balanced with his labor; or from labor if it is not balanced with his equipment.

The manager's real problem is to combine and balance all his costs so as to get the highest net profit from the combination. If from this book, or some other source, you have received the idea that the farm manager has many things to contend with, you are exactly right. Of course, in the broad applications of the law of diminishing returns, you see them all. That is why we call it "the guiding principle of management."

Of course, we should like to be more specific about what is the right combination of cost factors to be used for a successful farm. However, it is apparent that, more than for any other single difference among farms, there are six million "proper combinations" for six million farms. The right combination for any one can be determined only by studying the specific farm and the operator in detail—and then the answer would be as individual as a proper fit of eyeglasses.

The problem is very real. Because farms and farmers differ so widely, farm organization can be written about only in terms of principles, but it must be applied in specific detail. For example, as applied to the man rather than to the farm, note the

influence of management upon the proper size of farm: On page
176 we gave a formula:

$$\text{Price} - \text{Cost} = \text{Profit Margin.}$$

Now for this broader purpose, let us modify it to read:

$$\text{Volume} \times \text{Price} - \text{Cost} = \text{Net Profits.}$$

Contained within the terms of this formula are all the manager's objectives and problems. It is not an invariable rule that
the lowest cost per unit of product gives the highest net farm
profits; for example:

UNITS		PRICE		COST		NET PROFIT
1,000	$\times$	$5.00	—	3.00	=	$2,000;
800	$\times$	$5.00	—	2.75	=	$1,800.

To boost volume it may be desirable to bear somewhat more
than an absolute minimum cost per unit, but the range of this
permissible cost increase must be closely watched. If the $3.00 cost
above had increased to $3.25, net profits would have been reduced
to $1,750. C. L. Holmes has called agriculture an industry of "in-
creasing costs,"[5] meaning that as the size of farm businesses increase, costs characteristically increase and profits go down. The
degree to which this is true depends upon the ability of the manager to stave off diminishing returns as the size of his operation
increases.

Greater volume gives the opportunity for greater profits if
the manager has the talent to handle it (see Chapter 18).

The right size of farm is thus ten acres and a mule, if that is
all the manager is capable of handling. Or, for those rare managers
with proportional ability, it is hundreds of intensively operated
acres, hundreds of thousands of invested dollars, and a labor force
that reaches "factory" proportions.

In conclusion, we believe that the basic points of attack on the
problem of better farm organization are these:

1. The major item most farm families sell is their own labor.
It is sold in the form of products raised.

[5] C. L. Holmes, *Economics of Farm Organization and Management* (New
York, D. C. Heath and Company, 1928), 212.

Labor is hired to do the work the family cannot handle. Hired help is expected to increase profits; first, by producing more than it costs, and second, by increasing the accomplishment of family labor (for example, by harvesting a crop the family grew).

A profitable job for the operator and his family is the objective of all family-commercial farming. To attain it, all the labor used on the farm must be provided with an "environment" in which it can be productive; and that leads to the following principle.

2. Full productive employment for labor requires equipment (including service buildings). Equipment should be added to the labor force where it will save cost in comparison with labor that could be displaced. The right kinds and sizes of equipment will be whatever gives full employment to at least the minimum labor force, with the lowest labor-equipment combination cost in relation to what is raised. That leads to:

3. The labor-equipment combination must be applied to enough good land and good livestock to provide full productive employment. (Twelve months employment a year is the objective, with, of course, proper adjustments for your type of farming.)

Emphasis on good land leads to:

4. High quality soil and good soil management are increasingly important in successful farming. Probably this fact is more widely recognized than the reason back of it. Basically, it is because of the very great improvements that are being made in farm equipment, livestock, and crops.

It costs no more to operate equipment over a high-yielding acre than over a poor one. That was as true in grandfather's day as now; but the new, highly efficient mechanized equipment involves more cash-out-of-pocket expense than Dobbin did. Being cash expense, it is a first claim upon production. Therefore, more than formerly, it is the high-producing acre that will provide "income for living" after the expense checks have been written.

Or again, improved crop strains make their maximum contribution to profits when used on productive land. If hybrid corn adds 20 per cent to yields, on seventy-five bushel land the increase is fifteen bushels, on thirty-bushel land it is six bushels.

Maximum profits cannot be realized when high quality in one factor is combined with low quality in another. Under this condition the full productive value of the high-quality factor is not gained because diminishing returns set in so quickly on the low-quality factor. Thousands, if not indeed hundreds of thousands, of once-farmed acres have been forced out of farming for this very reason. They are acres that either were not, or could not, be improved fast enough to keep them in balance with improvements in equipment, crops, and livestock.

Farming is a long-time business. A very minor production handicap when one starts farming as a young man may grow into a major profit-killer before retirement age. By no means has an ultimate been attained in the improvement of crops, or animals, or farm machinery. Nor is there reason to believe that continued improvements will not require, in the future as in the past, corresponding improvement in soil productivity if full benefits are to be attained.

It is for these reasons that a young man should start farming on the most productive and most responsive soil he can acquire. It is good soil that is the foundation of a successful farm, for with it his labor and other high-quality production factors can be most profitably combined.

26. Farm Analysis—a Watchdog on the Business

FARM analysis has but one real purpose: to uncover the weaknesses of the business through which profits may leak away. Success or failure on a farm may be attributed to any number of wrong causes if the facts are not winnowed from mere opinions. Having established in the three preceding chapters what we believe are the main objectives and problems of farm organization, this task of analysis remains.

Specifically, these questions demand answers from you as the manager: (1) Are your resources being used effectively? (2)Is your enterprise response up to standard? (3) Where are your main points of attack to plug the profit-killing leaks and to strengthen the whole competitive position of your farm operations?

Patience and figuring are required, first, to find the facts about your business and, second, to find the standards (the measuring sticks) against which your results may be compared. Therefore, in the following calculations we are presenting detailed figures, not because they may have particular application to your own special problems but because they provide a definite method of approach. Whatever your type of farming and wherever you may be located, you should be able to adapt this method or a variation of it to the analysis of your own farm.

The farm with which we shall be immediately concerned is in Fulton County, Ohio, thirty miles west of Toledo. General crop and livestock farming predominates in the surrounding area. Incidentally, this is the region of the famous "Waldeck barn" which incorporates a covered barnyard within the structure of the barn itself.[1]

It is a successful and profitable farm. But why is it? The answer will be sought through separate answers to the following questions:

1. How adequate is the job for the labor force?
2. Are the farm enterprises well balanced?
3. Is the enterprise response up to standard?
4. How satisfactory is the accomplishment of the labor force?
5. Is the farm suitably equipped?   .
6. Is the soil being maintained?

As "measuring sticks" against which to compare this farm, we have drawn on information from the Ohio Agricultural Experiment Station, which has published a large amount of highly useful data for this kind of analysis. Wherever you may be located, your county agent and state experiment station can supply you with similar figures, which will at least approximately fit your own conditions.

First, a description of the Fulton County farm: It contains eighty acres, a size now less common in the area than formerly but still not uncommon. Seventy acres are cropland, laid out in five equal fields and used in a five-year rotation of corn, corn, oats, wheat, and clover. Six acres, once a woodlot and still containing a scattering of trees, are used for pasture. House, barns, garden, and three small hog lots cover the remaining four acres.

The main barn is 36x50 feet, with five horse stalls at one end

[1] See Russell Lord, *Men of Earth* (New York, Longmans, Green, and Company, 1932), 38.

and haymow above. Across a center drive another haymow extends from roof to floor. Attached to one end is a "milking barn," 30x30 feet with ten stanchions and three box stalls. Running back as an ell from the main barn (the milking barn opens into it also) is the covered barnyard typical of Fulton County. In this case it is a building 30x50 feet with concrete floor and straw loft above. All winter the cattle run loose in here except at milking time. They are bedded down with the straw from overhead. Here, protected by floor and roof, the winter's manure accumulates to be hauled on the land in the spring. Other buildings include a one-story 20x36-foot hen house, a hog house, and a tool shed.

Fluid milk is produced for the Toledo market. The dairy unit consists of eight cows and two heifers. A hog enterprise is carried on the two-litter system, with seven sows farrowing each March and September. The hogs are fed out to about 225 pounds, then sold on the local livestock auction. Three hundred chicks are raised each summer, and two hundred hens are housed each fall. Twice a week an egg buyer stops at the farm.

I. *The adequacy of the job.* In the analysis of any farm business, the logical first question is how adequate is the job presented to the labor force?

In this case the labor force is one man. Combining and corn picking are custom hired. For hauling hay and straw, labor is exchanged with a similarly situated neighbor. But no other help is hired, nor are there family workers except the operator himself.

Probably the best measure of his job adequacy is the number of full days of productive work provided by the farm. In the jargon of the farm-management specialist the unit of measurement is the "productive-man-work-unit," which is merely the amount of crop or livestock work turned out in a ten-hour day at average rates of accomplishment. If, for example, by the common farming methods of your state or locality, the yearly care of a dairy cow requires 140 hours of work, that would be fourteen ten-hour days, or fourteen work units. On this basis eight dairy cows would provide a farmer with 112 full days of productive work a year.

The work unit calculations for this particular farm are as follows:[2]

This dairyman has made only one concession to efficiency, the electric light. He is feeding and watering by hand. He is raising the feed up instead of delivering it down. A little concrete work and full utilization of electricity would increase yield, cut work input, add profits.

Alabama Herefords graze in manganese bur clover and Johnson grass. The clover provides winter and early spring grazing, Johnson grass handles spring and summer, or is cut for hay in June and the second growth grazed after it is "frosted" in late fall.

	Acres of crops and number of livestock on this farm	Average hours of labor per acre or per head in western Ohio*	Productive work units per acre or per head	Total productive man work units
Crop:				
Corn	28	23	2.3	64
Oats	14	12	1.2	17
Wheat	14	14	1.4	20
Clover	14	8	0.8	11
Livestock:				
Cows	8	140	14.0	112
Heifers	2	25	2.5	5
Brood sows	7	25	2.5	18
Pigs raised	91	5	0.5	45
Hens	150	170 per 100	17.0 per 100	25
Chicks raised	300	30 per 100	3.0 per 100	9

Total work units for the farm   326

* Source: U.S.D.A. Mimeographed Bulletin F. M. 40.

Note: The really significant calculation is how much productive work per man. In this case, 326 work units ÷ 1.0 man-equivalent = 326 work units per man.

This farmer is most certainly fully employed. At the usual rates of labor accomplishment on farms in this area, he would have a full ten hours of productive work to do each workday in the year. And it must be remembered that the "productive work" is not all the work on a farm. Necessary but not directly productive maintenance work requires about one-quarter of the total working time on Ohio farms.[3] Obviously this farmer is turning out his work in much less time per acre and per animal than the average of Ohio farmers. Not only is he fully employed, but also, assuming that his crop and livestock yields are near average, his rate of accom-

[2] One excellent reference giving annual labor requirements per acre of crops and per head of livestock in each state is M. R. Cooper et al., *Labor Requirements for Crops and Livestock* (U.S.D.A. Bureau of Agricultural Economics Mimeographed Bulletin F.M. 40, May, 1943). This bulletin gives crop and livestock labor requirements as of 1939. It might be hoped that such a valuable reference will be supplemented periodically to bring it up to date.

[3] John H. Sitterley, *Planning My Farm Business* (Ohio Agricultural Extension Bulletin 211, 1940), 27.

plishment is unusually high. Average productive work units per man in his type of farming are nearer to 240 than to 300.

II. *The enterprise balance.* Enterprise balance may be approached from at least three angles: seasonality of labor requirements; adjustment to market opportunity; and the relation of feed supplies to livestock numbers.

General crop and livestock farming usually gives good balance of seasonal labor needs. On specialized crop farms, by contrast, it is almost equally common to meet with peaks and valleys in the demands upon the labor force.

Following is the seasonal pattern of work on this Fulton County farm:

Crops:
   Oats—land prepared and crop planted in early April; harvested in late July.
   Corn—land prepared after oats are in; crop planted in mid-May; cultivated three times during June and early July; harvested in October.
   Clover—harvested between corn cultivations in mid-June.
   Wheat—land prepared in August; seeded in late September; harvested in July.
Livestock:
   Cows—provide work at all times throughout the year, somewhat less in summer than in winter.
   Hogs—sows farrow in March and September; feeding pigs continues throughout the year.
   Hens—small enterprise, therefore creating no labor problem; chicks started in April.

The summary of a labor distribution such as this is obviously easy. It creates no problems needing correction.

One market available to this farm is not being utilized, and certainly with the business he now has, there is no compulsion upon the operator to use it unless he chooses. Three miles from the farm is a vegetable cannery for which he could be growing tomatoes, sweet corn, or snap beans. Should he change his rotation to include these crops, he would have to reduce his livestock numbers. He would then have more summer work and less employment for himself in winter. He would need seasonal hired help.

Tomatoes could be substituted for some of his corn acreage, and all or part of his oats could be displaced with snap beans and sweet corn. To find out whether these adjustments would return more net profit than his present crops and livestock could (and should) be figured. Nevertheless, he now has all the work he can handle, and it is profitable, productive work. Since that is the case and if he prefers to be primarily a livestock farmer, there is certainly no overpowering reason for his changing to a more intensive rotation of crops.

His buildings are not now used as fully as they could be. Some space might readily be converted to permit him to keep more hens. The egg market available to him is a comparatively good one; but he could not keep much more poultry without buying feed and hiring labor. Particularly if he did the latter, he might have to increase his operations enough to employ fully another man in order to get dependable help and retain his present high labor efficiency. Unless he chooses, there seems to be no good reason why he should take on that problem.

All his crops except wheat are now marketed through livestock. He has taken advantage of the Toledo fluid-milk market. Grain feeds above the quantity needed by his cows are being fed profitably to his present numbers of hogs and hens.

Conclusion: This farmer's adjustment to markets is satisfactory.

How much livestock and what kinds present another question. How much feed is available? It is hardly the part of conservatism to stock a farm beyond the limit of its feed supplies. Especially is this true with pasture and roughages. "Most conservative and experienced operators plan to have slightly less livestock than their normal feed supply will carry. They thus have some leeway in feeding and may carry their livestock longer, feed heavier, sell the surplus feed, or hold until another season."[4]

Feed needs for the Fulton County farm have been calculated

[4] John H. Sitterley, *Feed Consumed by Livestock: A Guide for Planning Farm Organization* (Ohio Agricultural Extension Bulletin 203, 1940), 8.

from standards presented in Ohio Extension Bulletin 203. The requirements balance against production as follows:

Hay:

8 cows, 2½ tons each =	20 tons
2 heifers, 1½ tons each =	3 tons
Amount needed	23 tons
Amount produced	28 tons
Normal carryover	5 tons

Grain:

8 cows, 2,500 lbs. each =	20,000 lbs.
2 heifers, 500 lbs. each =	1,000 lbs.
7 brood sows, 2,250 lbs. each =	15,750 lbs.
91 pigs raised, 725 lbs. each =	65,975 lbs.
150 hens (av. no. for the year), 100 lbs. each =	15,000 lbs.
300 chicks raised, 18 lbs. per chick started	5,400 lbs.
Amount needed	123,125 lbs.
Purchase of protein supplement: 10% of cow ration, 6% of hog ration	7,000 lbs.
Balance, home-grown feed	116,125 lbs.

Of this total, about 7,000 pounds of wheat would be used for poultry. The balance, roughly 110,000 pounds, would be corn and oats.

Corn produced =	about 94,000 lbs.
Oats produced =	about 32,000 lbs.
Total	126,000 lbs.
Needed as feed	110,000 lbs.
Normal carryover	16,000 lbs.

From this excess over normal needs, oat seed (about 1,000 pounds) would come out, and the balance could be accumulated as "insurance," used up in a slightly higher rate of feeding, used for a slight increase in the number of animals, or sold.

Wheat produced =	about 490 bushels
Needed for poultry feed =	120 bushels
Needed for seed =	30 bushels
Balance (usually sold)	340 bushels

These calculations show the livestock program of the farm to be closely in line with feed production. A small margin of safety is allowed above normal needs.

In recent years two interesting changes have taken place in the livestock program of this farm. When five horses were kept, the cattle enterprise had to be very small because forage was not available. Later the power was two horses and a tractor and the dairy comprised six cows. Selling the last team permitted an increase to eight cows, and now even nine looks feasible. The other change came with the advent of hybrid corn and improved varieties of oats. Increased yields of approximately ten bushels per acre for each crop provided enough additional feed to increase the hog enterprise from five brood sows to seven.

III. *Is the enterprise response up to standard?* The point to be investigated here is crop and livestock yields in comparison with community averages. It is a vital matter in the success of the farm. "Average" yields seldom return more than a pittance of profit. High-producing acres and animals are profit-makers—unless fertilizer and feed should be used so lavishly as to offset the cost savings on land, labor, buildings, and machinery.

A major influence on crop yields is always soil quality and management. The soil on the Fulton County farm has been mapped as Wauseon fine sandy loam. This fact is, of course, meaningless until the characteristics of the soil are known. The Ohio Agricultural Experiment Station has reported it to have poor drainage and to be slightly acid. The farm has been fully tile drained, with tile lines every four rods. In addition it has been thoroughly limed, well manured, and fertilized. With these amendments to its natural characteristics, the soil scientists of the Ohio station have given it a crop productivity rating of 3, on a scale in which 1 is the best soil in Ohio, and 10 is the poorest.[5]

With this information we should logically expect the crop yields of the farm in question to be higher than the state average. Consequently, state averages would not be a suitable comparison for measuring this farmer's results. The best comparison would be with neighboring farmers having similar soils.

For the following tabulation we have used Fulton County averages;[6] since they are as near as we could get to the desired data for the farmer's own community.

	Five-year average crop yields and livestock production for:	
	FULTON COUNTY, OHIO	THIS FARM
Crop:		
Corn	50 bu.	60 bu.
Oats	50 bu.	70 bu.
Wheat	25 bu.	35 bu.
Clover	1.5 tons	2.0 tons
Livestock:		
Milk per cow	5,500 lbs.	8,000 lbs.
Pigs saved per litter	6.5	6.5
Eggs per hen	145	165

No serious weaknesses in crop yields or rates of livestock production show up in this tabulation. The enterprise response most outstanding relative to the county average is oats; least outstanding is hogs. That the soils of the farm may be somewhat better than the county average could be inferred from the comparison of all crop yields; but it must have been the manager and not the soil that boosted the cow and hen yields to their present level. The remaining question this manager should ask himself about his yields is: Are they as high as they should be on my farm? Yields relative to "the average" are clues, not answers.

IV. *How satisfactory is the accomplishment of the labor force?*

[5] G. W. Conrey and A. H. Paschall, *A Key to the Soils of Ohio* (Ohio Agricultural Experiment Station Special Circular No. 44, 1934), 21.

[6] Data from *Ohio Agricultural Statistics* (Ohio Agricultural Experiment Station, Bulletin 602, 1939) and similar publications for earlier years.

This point of analysis may seem similar to job adequacy as discussed above, but there is a very important difference.

If one man works 140 hours per cow and gets 5,500 pounds of milk, while another puts in the same amount of work but gets 8,000 pounds, the second man is obviously getting more output per hour. It is not enough to be "busy," or even to be busy at productive work. The pay-off is in accomplishment.

Man-work-units show how much productive work the labor force has to do. The combination of work units and rates of yield shows how much is accomplished. A calculation that brings these two previously determined factors together is therefore exceedingly worthwhile. To make it, we must fall back upon another of the technical tools of the farm-management specialist: the determination of output units.

Here is the method:[7] If average corn yields in Fulton County are fifty bushels an acre, and the average labor requirement is twenty-three hours per acre, then the average production for ten hours of labor is twenty-two bushels. This twenty-two bushels, being the output for a day's work, is thus one "output unit." One hundred bushels of corn at this average rate of labor accomplishment in Fulton County would be 4.6 output units (100 ÷ 22 = 4.6).

Output Units for Fulton County, Ohio

	Average yield	Average labor requirement	Output units
Crop:			
Corn	50 bu. per acre	23 hours per acre	4.6 per 100 bu.
Oats	45 bu. per acre	12 hours per acre	2.7 per 100 bu.
Wheat	25 bu. per acre	14 hours per acre	5.6 per 100 bu.
Clover	1.5 tons per acre	8 hours per acre	0.5 per ton
Livestock:			
Milk	5500 lbs. per cow	140 hours per cow	0.25 per cwt.
Eggs	145 per hen	1.7 hours per hen	1.4 per 100 doz.
Pigs (2 litters per sow)	2925 lbs. per sow	90 hours per sow and 2 litters	3.0 per 1,000 lbs. live weight of hogs

Using the output-unit factors as given above, we now find it

[7] See G. P. Scoville and S. W. Warren, *Labor Requirements for New York Crops and Livestock* (Cornell Agricultural Experiment Station A. E. 462, 1943).

possible to determine the accomplishment of the labor force on the particular farm we have been analyzing. This operator's 1,680 bushels of corn equals 77 output units (4.6 units per 100 bushels). The fact that he put in only 64 work units to get 77 output units shows that his actual accomplishment in producing corn was 20 per cent above the average for the county (77 ÷ 64 = 120).

Output Units for this Farm

	Quantity of product	Output units
Corn	1,680 bushels	77
Oats	980 bushels	26
Wheat	490 bushels	27
Clover	28 tons	14
Milk	64,000 pounds	160
Hogs (liveweight)	20,475 pounds	62
Eggs	2,060 dozens	29
Heifers*	2	5
Chicks raised*	300	9
Total output units		409

* Output units on this young stock are the same as work units.

We found previously that this farmer, working alone, accomplished 326 work units—meaning that he has an unusually large number of acres and animals for one man to care for. If he were getting average yields from his crops and livestock, his output units would be the same as his work units. However, here we find that because his yields are much above average, he is getting a total output equal to 409 average days of work, indeed an exceptional rate of accomplishment per man.

An "average" situation would be something like this: A man putting in 300 days of farm work a year at the average of work efficiency would do about 60 days of maintenance work and 240 days of productive work (240 productive work units). With average yields from the crops and livestock he works with, he will turn off 240 output units. But this average rate of labor accomplishment ordinarily will not pay wages. A minimum standard to strive for is 300 output units per man. Anything less will turn little profit.

V. *Is the farm suitably equipped?* Suitable equipment is the kind and amount that permit the farmer to get the work done efficiently and on time without unduly high equipment costs.

The farm with which we are concerned is equipped with a two-plow general purpose tractor (no horses). Other machinery includes two-bottom plow, seven-foot double disk, twelve-foot spike-tooth harrow, cultipacker, grain drill, corn planter, two-row cultivator, mower, side-delivery rake, hay loader, manure spreader, rubber-tired wagon, and a trailer for the family car. At approximate 1940–42 prices, this line of equipment would have cost about $2,400 if purchased new. On most farms the average value of the equipment would be depreciated, at any one time, about halfway to its "junk" value. So figured, the current inventory value of this equipment would be about 60 per cent of $2,400, or $1,440.

This figure is necessary for the farm analysis but is not very informative until one gets a yardstick against which to compare

Power and Machinery Investment and Costs

	This farm	Thirteen Miami County farms using tractor power only
Acres of crops	70	70
Man work units	326	282
Power and machinery investment:		
Tractor	$ 600	$ 573
Machinery	840	554
Total	$1,440	$1,127
Per crop acre	$ 20.57	$ 16.10
Annual power and machinery costs		
Tractor	$ 200*	$ 157
Machinery	210*	138
Total	$ 410	$ 295
Per crop acre	$ 5.86	$ 4.21
Per man work unit	$ 1.26	$ 1.05

* The tractor on this farm is used about 400 hours per year; on the average of the Miami County farms, 312 hours.

Actual tractor and machinery operating costs are not available for the Fulton County farm. Therefore, we have figured the tractor at the same cost per hour as in Miami County, and the other machinery costs at the same percentage of the inventory value.

it. For that purpose we will use, as being the best data available, figures on equipment investment and costs for a group of farms of similar size in Miami County, Ohio.[8]

Using the Miami County figures as the yardstick may not be entirely satisfactory, but in the absence of other comparisons, these do furnish some clues. The Fulton County farmer has a higher equipment investment and somewhat more cost per acre. Yet when the two are compared on the basis of the amount of productive work to be done, his power and machinery costs certainly are not seriously out of line.

VI. *Is the soil being maintained?* From the standpoint of current income, other points in the farm analysis may be more important than this, but in the long view the vital question of soil maintenance stands at the top.

How various crops influence soil productivity has been reported by Salter, Lewis, and Slipher from the Ohio Experiment Station.[9] Perhaps their findings do not exactly fit this Fulton County farm, but at least they do provide a starting point for figuring its productivity balance.

The rotation of corn, corn, oats, wheat, and clover is a hard one on the soil. Corn has a depleting influence of about 2 per cent a year; oats and wheat, 1 per cent. Clover, on the other hand, has a soil-building effect sufficient to offset one crop of corn. Thus the productivity indexes for this rotation are, -2, -2, -1, -1, $+2$, or a net depletion of 4 per cent in five years.

Offsetting plus-values are manure and fertilizer. The Ohio soil scientists report one ton of manure or two hundred pounds of "average" commercial fertilizer per acre to add one-eighth of 1 per cent to the annual balance of soil productivity. Consequently, on this and other livestock farms, the amount of manure available becomes a question of major importance.

An exact answer is difficult to determine, but an approximation can be made after figuring the number of animal units on

8 See F. L. Morison and Ross V. Baumann. *Labor, Power, and Machinery on Small Farms in Ohio* (Ohio Agricultural Experiment Station Bulletin 628, 1942).

9 Refer to the discussion and figures on pages 00-00.

the farm. Each animal unit produces about twelve tons of manure (including bedding) annually. The proportion recovered for use on cropland will vary with pasturing practices and the method of manure handling. In northern Ohio, and particularly with the protection afforded by the covered barnyard, the recovery may well run 8 to 10 tons.[10]

An animal unit is one mature cow or horse, or proportionate numbers of other livestock. The following conversion factors apply fairly well to Ohio but would need to be changed somewhat for certain other parts of the country. (Check with your experiment station.)

Animal	Animal units per head
Cow, bull, horse, or mule	1.0
Heifer or colt	0.5
Brood sow	0.33
Pig raised	0.1
Hens	1.0 per 100
Pullets raised	3.0 per 1,000

Thus the Fulton County farm is found to have 22.4 animal units. An estimated recovery of ten tons of manure per animal unit may be a little high. If it is obtained, however, each crop acre on the farm gets fifteen tons in the course of the rotation, or an average of three tons per year. In addition, fertilizer is being used on the wheat and on each crop of corn at the rate of two hundred pounds of a 2–12–6 analysis. Thus the summary of the present productivity balance per five-year rotation is as follows:

Net effect of the crop sequence	−4.0 per cent
Added through 15 tons of manure	+1.875 per cent
Added through 600 pounds of fertilizer	+0.375 per cent
Productivity balance (per five-year rotation)	−1.75 per cent

Here is the first major weakness that has appeared in the

[10] John A. Slipher, in *Manure: Its Management in Barn and Field* (Ohio Extension Bulletin 262, 1945), 5, gives other methods of approximating the manure tonnage on a farm:

    1. Tons of feed (barn dry) $\times$ 1.7 = tonnage of manure.

    2. Tons of livestock $\times$ months fed + tons of bedding = tonnage of manure.

analysis of this farm. It seems to be serious; a situation that cannot be continued indefinitely without disastrous consequences in lowered yields, a reduced capacity to carry livestock, a consequent reduction in available manure, further decline in yields, and all the characteristics of a vicious profit-killing circle.[11]

That, of course, is the long-time sequence. One or two rotations, even three or four, may not show it in marked degree, particularly if continued improvement in crop strains tends to hold higher yields. Perhaps, also, such statements are mere "viewing with alarm." It might be that the crop depletion indexes used above are too great for this farm. Such a fact is hinted by the fine-sandy-loam soil. Though the organic content should trend downward, a sandy loam does not lose tilth so quickly as a silt or a clay loam; that is, it presents less serious problems of "physical" maintenance.

No extenuating circumstance of this sort should encourage complacency, however. A productivity balance so much out of balance is certainly warning to stop, look, and listen. And an observant operator can tell whether his soil is becoming harder, more compact, less easy to work, and whether his crop response is declining.

What positive steps, if any, may be taken? This farmer cannot readily carry more livestock to provide more manure. Neither can he change his rotation to one corn crop and two legume crops without changing his whole farm organization. What less drastic steps? More fertilizer, for one! An additional 2,800 pounds per rotation would be needed to balance the indicated fertility decline.

Or, an added plus value might be achieved by changing his hay seeding mixture. He is now using red clover and timothy. (The timothy does not make much growth when left down only one year; therefore, his hay is mainly clover.) The timothy is seeded in the fall with the wheat; the clover, early the following spring. But red clover is a biennial. It dies out the second winter. Therefore, it is only a dead legume sod that is plowed down for corn; and it contributes less to the soil than would green and growing perennial legumes. Shifting to alfalfa and ladino would be an advantage in this direction, as well as yielding normally both more and better

[11] The situation would be even worse if, instead of being flat, these crop fields were rolling to a degree that made them erosive.

hay. The change in the legume seeding might be from twelve pounds of red clover per acre to six pounds of alfalfa, three of red clover, and one of ladino clover. The result should be a boost in the soil building value of the hay crop in the rotation from the present +2.0 to +2.5.

Another possible step in reducing the fertility imbalance without changing the rotation itself would be to seed a legume cover crop (preferably yellow-blossom, biennial sweet clover in this area) between the two corn crops. If seeded in the first corn crop, ten to fifteen pounds of scarified seed per acre, at the time the corn is laid by, and given a break on weather, it might well make a growth that would add a further three-quarters of 1 per cent to fertility.

Any or all of the above suggestions are possible adjustments away from a potentially if not actually critical situation. To make the right adjustment is the mark of a truly good and foresighted manager.

The fact is that on a great many farms one finds fertility imbalance not so greatly different from this case. To correct it by changing the whole existing farm organization is often not feasible. There usually are less drastic adjustments to head off disaster— which, of course, must be adapted to local condition. Check the possibilities with your state extension agronomist or soil conservationist.

To repeat, we have presented these six points of analysis at length because we think you can use the method, with or without adjustments, in analyzing your own farm. If it is carefully done, there will be no major weaknesses in your business that you won't uncover. We invite you to try it during your slack work season. You will uncover the profit-builders in your operations and the profit-killers. Then, strengthen the first; eliminate the second.

You will need three aids: (1) a willingness to undertake the job; (2) comparative figures from other farms against which you can check your own results (They should be from as near home as possible, and for your own type of farming. Get them from your county agent or state experiment station); and (3) records preferably or, lacking them, your best estimates on your own farm operations.

27. Farm Accounts—What and Why?

AN exploding poof—a cloud of smoke and dust—then another Midwest barn crackled into a blaze. As the flames sucked through the hay chutes and ate into the tindery fodder, the farmer hustled out his livestock, then salvaged just one other item, the granary door. Over its inner surface were closely penciled figures— his only record of twenty-odd years of farming. He rehung the door in the new barn built on the foundations of the old, and there the door continued to be his "ready reference" on past operations.

This door was not unique, unless possibly in the quantity of notes written on it. Its near counterpart is to be found on many another granary, packing shed, shop, and milk room. The records thereon are generally interesting but of little practical use. Only the unusual gets written down. You might find, "Corn lot back of orchard went 90 bushels to the acre."

"What year was that?" you ask.

"Let's see, now. That was the year FDR was elected." Even after you work on that clue, the answer is not very helpful. The ninety-bushel yield turns out to be a high-water mark, the best piece of corn the farm ever produced. No one ever kept records complete enough to determine the average corn yield for the farm, to say nothing of yield figures for the different fields.

It is not only barn-door accounting that is of little use in managing a farm. The next most common type, the diary record, falls much in the same category. A diary is difficult to use as a reference. You may hunt through every entry in the month of June for a certain item. You are sure it is there. When in exasperation you are about to give up, you find it under April. However carefully you keep the diary, it is almost impossible to summarize and analyze so that you get a concise picture of the farm operations for the year.

Practically every farmer keeps records of a sort—perhaps a check book, a spindle for bills, the ubiquitous diary, or the blank pages in the almanac. Nothing before in history has done so much as the income tax to stimulate farmer interest in keeping books. "How much did you take in? How much were your expenses?" become vital questions as each January fifteenth approaches. But records for income-tax returns are actually much less important than records as an aid to management. As a commercial farmer you need them for the same reasons that other businessmen need them: (1) to determine whether or not you made a profit, and how much (The change in your bank balance during the year does not tell you.); (2) to help uncover and eliminate conditions within the farm business that result in loss, and to further develop your sources of profit (This is by far the most important reason for keeping records.); and (3) to simplify the preparation of income-tax returns.

The most common mistake in farm accounting, next to keeping no records at all, is trying to keep too many. It is an easy matter, all too easy, to start a more complicated system of accounts than will ever be completed or summarized. The point we wish strongly to emphasize is this: Accounts are not worth the paper they are written on unless you use them. It takes time to keep them and more time to summarize them. They are a tool of management justifiable only to the degree they serve management. They serve management not at all if you get disgusted halfway through the year and drop the whole complicated project. Fully recognizing that some persons are exceptions to any rule and wishing in no way to discourage the exceptions, we still say: Unless the size of your operation will justify a bookkeeper, do not attempt double-entry accounts or detailed cost accounts. Keep your bookkeeping simple. It can be done and still give you much information both for analyzing and controlling the farm business and for the management of income taxes.

The most basic of all farm records, highly valuable in itself and an essential part of a more complete account system, is a farm inventory. The inventory is merely a list of the quantity and the value of all property used in the farm business—the real estate, livestock, equipment, supplies, accounts receivable for items sold, working capital on hand, and so forth. Against these assets are balanced all the liabilities of the farmer—the accounts, notes, and mortgages owed. The amount by which the assets exceed the liabilities is the net worth of the farmer. In other words, the inventory, as the term is used in farm accounting, is comparable to the balance sheet in business accounting.

The inventory shows, of course, what you own, what you owe,

and what your net worth is at a certain time. It should be taken on or close to the first day of the year, or the first day of whatever fiscal year is found to be most convenient on your farm. On most farms it can be taken in a half-day or less, and no other farm record you can keep will provide so much information for so little effort. It can be used directly as a credit statement with your banker, and if carefully done each year, will be a potent factor in building your credit standing. The change from one year's inventory to the next will show how much you are getting ahead (or going behind, which is equally important to know).

A farm-inventory form can probably be obtained from your county agent or your bank. In most regions you can get one by writing to your state agricultural college. Some forms are set up so that you can accumulate three, four, or five years' inventories in one booklet—an arrangement which is very convenient for making comparisons of one year with another.

Wilson Gee has quoted the following story from *The Progressive Farmer*, Raleigh, North Carolina:

"Does it pay to make a farm inventory each year?

"Well, here's a partial answer. Some years ago a banker friend was telling of an experience he had. At the beginning of the year he had made a loan to a young farmer who was starting out just about from scratch. At the end of the year the young man came in showing very plainly that he was badly discouraged. Because of drouth he had not made the crops he expected to make, and he could make only a partial payment on the note. It would soon be time to make arrangements for next year and he felt he was worse off now than when he started. Frankly, the young man was ready to give up.

" 'Wait just a minute,' said the banker as he reached for the record that was made out and filed when the loan was made. 'How many cows do you have now? How many calves?' On completing the check-up they found the young man had more livestock than he had when the loan was made, more corn in the crib, more hay in the loft, and he still had the mule and implements he had bought with a part of the money obtained through the loan. He had been building up his capital.

" 'Why, young man, you are a better credit risk now than you were a year ago,' announced the banker. 'Your net worth is greater. The increase in value of livestock, feed, and equipment far exceeds the unpaid balance of your note.'

"A very much relieved young man left the office of the banker, all because of a few minutes work with a lead pencil. Why not try this plan around New Year's? Nothing will pay better the next rainy day."[1]

One object lesson this story teaches applies to all farm accounting: Record quantities as well as values. Value figures are perishable, because prices change. Five hundred bushels of corn may be worth $300 at one time, $600 at another, but the quantity is always 500 bushels of corn. If your inventories show only dollar amounts, you will not know whether changes in your figures from one time to another are changes in price or changes in quantity. Analysis of your results will be "stymied." Likewise, in the case of purchases and sales, the record of physical quantities is as important, if not more important, than the dollars. The reason is that farm analysis must be largely in terms of quantities rather than prices.

Valuable as the annual inventory is, it is not adequate for the proper management of the farm. It should be supplemented at least by crop and livestock records and by a classified cash account. Adequate crop records may well begin with a farm map, a separate one for each year. Kind and acreage of crop may be recorded field by field. On the margin or back of the map, blank spaces may be prepared for recording crop yields. Other spaces may be used for a field-by-field record of lime, fertilizer, and manure applications, cover crops plowed down, and other soil treatments. Such facts are surprisingly difficult to remember more than a year or two back. Consequently the record becomes increasingly useful for observing trends in crop yields as years go by.

Livestock records may show a summary of feeds used for each type of animal: pig crop, lamb and calf crops, heifers freshened for the first time, number and weight of animals raised, number of pullets put in laying house, and a monthly record of livestock mortality. Records such as these are simple to keep and are ex-

1 Wilson Gee, *The Social Economics of Agriculture* (copyright 1932 and 1942 by The Macmillan Company, New York), 162.

tremely valuable in the farm analysis. If you use an account book that does not provide spaces for the items, they may be kept on separate sheets pinned or pasted in. An all too common fault in farm bookkeeping is to neglect items not provided for on the account forms used. Don't be limited by the book. Either get another that fits your needs, or insert pages ruled to suit yourself.

The simplest of all farm financial records is the classified cash account. It is easy to keep, to summarize and study. A common form is a double-paged spread, with income columns on one side, expense columns on the other. For example:

FARM RECEIPTS

Date	Description and quantity (State quantity sold)	Amount of Receipts	Eggs	Chickens	Hogs	Cream	Potatoes
1945 October							
1	100 bu. No. 1 potatoes	$150.00					$150.00
4	4 cases eggs (120 doz.)	66.00	$66.00				
4	150 bu No. 1 potatoes	225.00					225.00
8	6 hogs (1,380 lbs.)	196.65			$196.65		
8	5 cases eggs (150 doz.)	83.25	83.25				
11	3 " " (90 doz.)	49.95	49.95				
13	52 hens (281 lbs.)	89.92		$89.92			
	(etc. to fill the page)						
	Page totals	$860.77	$199.20	$89.92	$196.65		$375.00

Numerous cash-account books that use essentially this system are available from agricultural colleges, equipment and feed companies, and other farm service agencies. Some of them have the column headings written in. Others are left blank so that you may fill in the headings required for your own business. If the headings are there and do not fit your farm, strike them out and write in the headings you want.

You can make your own account book and provide whatever number of columns you need by ruling up blank paper in the manner illustrated, or you can get paper already ruled from most stationery stores (it is known as columnar journal paper). It is available with as many as twenty columns. Convenience dictates, however, that you should use as few columns as will give you a satisfactory breakdown of your income and expense items.

In using a form of this kind: (1) Be sure to give description and quantity. (2) Enter every item in the first column headed "amount of receipts" (or expense). Then enter it again under the proper classified heading. (3) Add all the columns, and then check the accuracy of your figures by adding the totals of the classified columns which should check with the total of the "amount" column. (4) Carry the page totals to a summary sheet, where with other page totals they may be added to get yearly totals.

A prepared account book, if you can find one to suit you, may be more convenient than making your own because probably it will include summary and analysis forms that will be very helpful in getting a concise and useful picture of your year's operations. An unorganized mass of figures is of little help until summarized and digested.

This system of accounts is much simpler, and for most farms fully as satisfactory as double-entry books in which each transaction must first be entered in a journal and then transferred to a ledger. Moreover, it is far easier to summarize at the end of the year.

The expense sheet should be set up similar to the one already given for receipts:

FARM EXPENSES

Date	Description and quantity (State quantity bought)	Amount of Expense	Labor	Feed	Gas & Oil	Equip-ment	Building Repairs	Seed & Fertilizer
1945 October								
1	Art Jones – wages for Sept.	$125 00	$125 00					
3	500 Gals. gasoline	85 00			$ 85 00			
3	4 plow points, 1 manure fork	8 30				$ 8 30		
3	1 ton hen mash	80 00		$ 80 00				
	(etc to fill the page)							
	Page totals	$298 30	$125 00	$ 80 00	$ 85 00	$ 8 30		

The column headings used on your expense sheets may be the same as those listed on the income-tax blank (1040 F), or you may, even for income-tax reports, use such other headings as will fit your own needs. The expense classification on the income-tax form is "suggestive," but not required.

With inventories for the beginning and end of the year, crop and livestock records, and classified cash account as suggested above, you will be prepared to make an analysis of your business similar to that presented in Chapter 26. You will have a classified breakdown of receipts and expenses for tax reporting. You will be able to figure the net profits for your farm business as a whole. You will know your change in net worth from the previous year. Records of this nature, if carefully studied, will permit you to do a better job of management than if these facts are mere guesses or blind spots. The analysis alone (Chapter 26), done on a stormy winter day, can be the most profitable day's work in the whole year.

What these suggested records will not permit you to do is to figure the unit cost of producing the different products that you raise, and the net profits from each of your several enterprises. The only records adequate for that purpose are complete cost accounts.

Certainly it is possible that the hens may be a losing proposition on your farm, while the hogs are the real money-makers. Or, your cows may be showing a loss, and your potatoes are supporting both you and the cows. Cost accounts, if you had them, would show up such facts. There is no question that cost accounts are valuable to a farmer. The only question is whether they are practicable. They require an enormous amount of "internal" bookkeeping; that is, of credits and charges back and forth between the various crop and livestock enterprises that make up your business. Each crop and livestock becomes a separate account in your books. Land, buildings, power, equipment, and so on, are set up as capital accounts. Feeds, seeds, fertilizers, spray materials, containers, and the like, in cases where you cannot charge them directly to a production account, have to be set up in "convenience" accounts.

Keeping cost-account records during the year is not so difficult as closing and summarizing them at the year's end. Then each crop account must be charged with its proportionate share of land costs, building costs, labor, power, equipment, seed, fertilizer and manure, spray materials, containers, interest, and miscellaneous overhead. It is credited with quantities and values sold, used in the household, fed to livestock, and carried over in the end inventory. Each livestock account is handled similarly. Each capital and convenience account must be closed separately, with the charges going to the production enterprises that used them. To the uninitiated, the whole system can become a nightmare of cross-entries and confused figures.

Farm cost accounting, as carried on by a number of the agricultural experiment stations over the country, is primarily a research procedure. Trained personnel is hired to do the job. The objective is to determine in detail the costs involved in producing various crops and livestock under actual farm conditions. The precisely determined figures are not, of course, exactly applicable to any farm except the ones involved; but that fact does not invalidate, or even limit the usefulness of the cost studies. Any farmer who has similar enterprises can learn much about his own business by studying the cost-account publications of the experiment stations. He may use the cost-account results to determine whether his own crop yields, livestock response, labor accomplishments, and equipment costs, are up to standard. He can then translate directly into his own business much of the cost-account findings concerning the relative profitableness of various alternative crop and livestock enterprises.

One of the authors has had considerable experience (mostly unsatisfactory) in helping individual "dirt" farmers set up cost-accounting systems where they planned to take over the job of closing and summarizing the accounts themselves.[2] On only two farms were they continued. One of these farmers had worked as an accountant before he bought his farm. The other operated a large business for which he hired a full-time bookkeeper. For the reasons we have set forth, our conclusion is that most farmers should not attempt cost accounting on their own farms. More satisfactory results will usually be obtained from doing a good job with the less complicated record system outlined on the preceding pages.

There is one other record, however, that we would recommend to almost any farmer, and that is a labor book. This could be an ordinary notebook with loose-leaf pages ruled as shown below. Separate pages, tabbed at the margin for quick reference, could be used for each crop and livestock. Daily entries on the appropriate sheets not only would serve as a record of the jobs done but could be a useful reference from one year to the next of when the jobs were done. At the year's end the total labor recorded on these sheets would show not only how much was used by each enterprise but also the total work done on the farm. To keep the record

[2] See page 232 for city farmers' accounts.

complete, sheets should be included for equipment repairs, building repairs, fences, woodlot, and similar items.

LABOR RECORD ON *Clover Hay*

Date	Job	Field Number	Man Hours	Horse Hours	Tractor Hours	Truck Miles	Notes
1945 June							
20	Mowing	2	5		5		
21	Raking	2	4		4		
22	Hauling	2	8		4		4 loads in cow barn
23	Hauling	2	16		8		8 loads in cow barn

(etc. to include all work on this enterprise)

Chore work on livestock, which is generally about the same from day to day through any one month, might reasonably be entered as one figure for each month. Work other than chores could be recorded daily. Other useful entries on the various enterprise sheets might include notes on when livestock are turned to pasture in the spring and taken off in the fall, when turned into various pasture fields, when rams are turned with the ewes, when pullets are put in the laying house (and how many), when orchards begin to bloom and reach full bloom, and weather conditions during the blooming period. Facts of this sort, if readily available, can be repeatedly useful to the manager of any farm.

Records and accounts on any farm must give recognition to the problem of income taxes. Tax rates have reached a point where income taxes have become a major management problem. "No productive farm can now be most effectively managed," says True D. Morse, "unless the effect of income taxes are constantly taken into consideration."[3]

Present tax rates should encourage farmers to be fairly cautious. As a farmer, you do have the privilege of charging losses back against the taxes of the two preceding years, or failing that, you may carry them forward two years. But if you have profits, Uncle Sam takes a considerable slice.

One successful vegetable grower of our acquaintance turned down the opportunity to buy some adjoining acreage at a very

[3] True D. Morse, "Farm Income Tax Management," *Journal of the American Society of Farm Managers and Rural Appraisers*, April, 1944, 41.

favorable price. He figured that good years would shove him into an income-tax bracket where he would not have enough left to offset the inevitable poor years in his type of farming.

Morse points out that "the amount of income tax paid by a taxpayer is the result of—

1. The tax law, and
2. The items subject to tax

"The taxpayer can do little about the law; but can so regulate his business as to control taxable items in a way to keep taxes to a minimum. The minimum tax is the just one to pay. The Government by law and by careful recheck by paid experts sees that the taxpayer does not pay less than he should but does nothing to prevent the taxpayer from paying too much. It is the business of the one who must pay taxes to see that he does not pay too much."[4]

Spending to save may be good business. It is necessary, of course, that the expenditures shall be for items that are legitimate expenses, and that they will put the farm and its equipment into better condition for future production. Here are illustrations based upon 1945 tax rates adapted from figures given by Morse in the article quoted above:

Item	Price	*Your actual cost when your net taxable income is:*		
		$2,000 or less	$2,000 to $4,000	$8,000 to $10,000
Lime	$ 5.00	$ 3.85	$ 3.80	$ 3.55
Fertilizer	40.00	30.80	30.40	28.40
Repairs	100.00	77.00	76.00	71.00
Damming, terracing, tiling, or other soil conservation	500.00	385.00	380.00	355.00

When taxable earnings are used for deductible expenditures, you get, in effect, a discount equal to your tax rate. The higher your tax bracket, the greater your discount. Note, however, the substantial discount on even the lowest surtax bracket. The moral is plain: Anticipate your necessary repairs, soil improvements,

4 "Farm Income Tax Management," *Journal of the American Society of Farm Managers and Rural Appraisers*, April, 1944, 42.

and so on, at times when you have taxable income. You get no discounts when you spend "no-profit" dollars.

Obviously, if you are to take advantage of your high-income years for making repairs, you must be able to approximate what your taxable income is going to be early enough that the expenditures can be made before the end of the year. Your accounts will have to be kept up to date and studied well in advance, or you will find yourself in the position of "if I had only known."

Another consideration which may influence the amount of your income tax is the method by which you report. As a farmer, you have the privilege of preparing your tax returns on either a "cash" basis or an "accrual" basis. The cash basis is the more simple method, but it has disadvantages. You report all income actually received and all expenditures actually paid out within the year, regardless of whether or not they apply to that particular year. Thus, if you sell stored crops or livestock from your feed lot so that your income is abnormally large for that year, you pay tax on that income. In other words, that income is taxed in the year during which actual cash is received. Morse says: "With the high surtaxes now in use and which are certain to be continued, this can easily result in paying excess taxes over a period of years. The cash basis should be used for farms only when the business is very small and/or the income and expenses are regular from year to year.

"The accrual basis of filing income tax returns should be used on farms where operations are large or complicated or where there may be large periodic purchases or marketings. This includes farms where livestock, particularly livestock feeding, is a major enterprise and where crops may be stored for future sale.

"The accrual basis is the method most certain to avoid the payment of excess taxes, and keep the payment of income taxes on the most reasonable basis from year to year.

"The accrual basis reports income as of the time it is earned and expenses as of the time they are incurred, regardless of the time that either may actually be paid."[5] That is, on accrual reports you pay tax on only the current year's business. Income items include cash sales, inventory increases (carryovers), and produce sold on credit even though you have not been paid. Expenses include

5 "Farm Income Tax Management," *Journal of the American Society of Farm Managers and Rural Appraisers*, Vol. VIII, No. 1 (April, 1944), 43.

cash expenditures, inventory decreases, and credit purchases not paid for.

Either method of income-tax reporting may be based upon the system of accounts suggested earlier in this chapter. For a cash-basis report, only the classified cash account would be needed. For an accrual report, the cash account and the inventories (including accounts receivable and accounts payable) would be required.

While it is true that you have your choice of cash or accrual reporting, if you wish to change from one to the other, you must get permission from the Commissioner of Internal Revenue to do so. Application for permission must be made within the first ninety days of the year for which the new basis of reporting is desired. Therefore, if you can, start your income-tax reporting on the basis which you wish to continue.

In spite of the emphasis given to taxes, we repeat our belief that records and accounts are of greater value in the analysis and management of the farm than in the management of taxes. Today's commercial farming is a business of growing complexity. It is in the neck-twisting position of ever looking backward to find its directions in past experience, and ever looking ahead to anticipate the changing conditions it is certain to meet. Few other businesses must look so far ahead. Agriculture is a business of slow turnover. A crop planted in the spring offers no alternative than to live with the decision back of that planting until it is time to plant again. A decision to buy certain livestock may be a commitment which cannot profitably be liquidated for several years. Planting an orchard may prove to be a commitment for a lifetime.

Where do you find directions except in the analysis of what has been and what now is? From these sighting points you look ahead and try to guess the bends in the road. Before the ink is dry in your account book, that record is history; but it shows you where you were. Without accounts you do not know. There is no way to project a trend you cannot see.

It is not enough to study your own accounts. No one farm (commercial farm) is operated in isolation from the influences that are affecting all farms. What may be happening on other farms is important to you. The basic question is: What are the trends in your type of farming? The answer is found in broad study outside your own business—in the farm press and in the reports of the

U.S.D.A. and the experiment stations. Your records, if they are the right ones, will tell you whether you are in line with the "standards" and with the trends. Though the study of your records is merely an analysis of past operations, it should help you to look ahead, to adjust your farm organization, and to inaugurate changes that will increase your future profits.

Addendum—Accounts for City Farmers

BECAUSE the number of city farmers, or nonworking farm owners, has now reached an impressive total and the trend toward absentee ownership shows signs of becoming permanent, a note on the kind of account-keeping desired by this class of owners is in order.

While one of the authors has been working for years in setting up, operating, and analyzing records on individual "dirt-farmer" businesses, the other has been designing and putting into effect tailored-to-measure bookkeeping systems for city farmers and big commercial operations. The essential difference in the two types of accounting (and this statement must be taken as an opinion, not as a rule) is that while it is generally possible and usually feasible to use a standard plan or variant thereof for the typical owner-operated family farm, this kind of record is nearly always inadequate for the absentee owner or large commercial operator. Therefore, in the latter case it is best to design a system to fit the individual project.

From the vantage point of having set up many a system of this sort, we stress again this rule: *Keep it simple.* Frequently the accounts are too many and lend themselves to fact-finding very unreadily, thus making the cost of securing the information greater than its value.

The kind of records and answers the average city farmer wants is the kind he demands and gets in his urban business. For it, however, he has a whole army of bookkeepers, fact-finders, inventory-control clerks, and other trained employees. Each process in his factory or business has one or more persons keeping a running record of every item used. On a farm, unless it is the rare giant operation—such as the Seabrook operation, which is the world's largest vegetable farm-and-processing plant—the cost of securing data would increase the overhead until the farm could not pay off in generations.

This seems to hint that a certain amount of "playing by ear" is inevitable in farm record keeping; as such, it certainly seems unscientific and unbusinesslike, and, on the face of it, runs counter to much that has been said in the foregoing chapters. The charge must be admitted to a degree. The authors know from only too much everyday, down-in-the-furrow experience that fine laboratory controls rarely ever are capable of transference to the fields as a whole. Somewhere along the line, you have to drop the beauties of the perfect system, perfectly executed, for a bit of playing by ear, or gambling if you will, unless you can afford to have the inexorable overhead catch up with you.

Let's take an example from actual experience of how the search for a cost figure that would be equal in veracity to a similar one in business caused real trouble. Admittedly, we are using a *reductio ad absurdum*. A farm-owner client of one of the authors (both, incidentally, worked on this particular problem) boasted to a business associate that he could find to a fraction of a cent just exactly what it cost him to grow corn. The business associate, a one-time farm boy, bet that the first man could do no such thing if the bettor was allowed to question the cost-searchers (in this case the authors).

The researchers paled at the thought, but the client was adamant. He could get such a figure in his urban business on a moment's notice. In his estimation, his farm was a much less complicated business than his urban affairs. He was told that the finding of this decimal figure was in reality impossible and, moreover, was not worth the expense, when a fairly good approximate figure was at hand from the everyday records. But the client had made his boast and would have none of approximations.

Here are some of the items that had to be considered: What was the real land rent? That meant finding out original cost, improvements (fertilizer, cover crops, drainage, fencing, etc.), taxes, interest on investment, residual value of previous crop (or soil loss), value of any income credited to the field after corn was off, such as stover pastured or plowed under.

Then came the cost of seed, fertilizer, seedbed preparation

(with a long, onerous analysis of the "equipment-operation" account to find just how much depreciation, gas and oil, repairs, and insurance should be charged). Next were costs of cultivating, corn-borer control, harvesting, hauling, cribbing, shrinkage, shelling, and building use.

Since we feared the questioner, we set up a charge to management, a charge to general overhead, and, to avoid any future tour de force on the part of the client, we figured our own charges on the cost-per-bushel basis. Our client won his bet only because his opponent knew it would cost him more than the bet to prove us wrong. The sole valuable result of this curious business was that we were fairly certain it cost $0.7125 per bushel to grow corn on that farm when corn could be bought by the carload, laid down on the farm in the bin, for $0.61 at that time.

This result does, however, emphasize the real value of more intensive accounting on non owner-operated or big-business farms. The city farmer should keep in mind that, unlike the "dirt farmer," he is not operating primarily as a means of selling his own labor; and, therefore, he should ask himself whether in reality it costs him more to grow certain feedstuffs than to buy them. If more city farmers understood this distinction before they bought their farms, there would undoubtedly be fewer of them—and fewer farm consultants whose business it is to try to make a profit grow where all factors are against them.

We have found that, from a standpoint of psychology if not of accounting practice, the first act in setting up a system of accounts for a large operation is to convince the owner that his home (if it is on the land) and its grounds should be eliminated from the figuring. Either their value can be subtracted from the total, or it can be included and rent charged on the books to the owner. If rent is charged, the "big house" becomes depreciable.

Next, the owner should be convinced that the various odd jobs around the house and grounds are not to be done by farm labor in "spare time." Modern farm laborers work on an hourly basis. When quitting time comes, even though there are several hours of daylight left, they have no interest in doing and should not be expected to do a few tasks for the boss—without compensation.

When the owner understands that he is not owning and operating a home free, as he so fondly likes to believe, a good start toward getting some realistic cost figures on the farm business is possible; otherwise, no matter what records are kept or how much time is spent, the figures achieved will be just about as much in accord with facts as a Grimm fairy tale.

The next step is to set up inventory and depreciation accounts. The plan for the equipment account then should be devised. You can go to extreme lengths here, but it is doubtful whether the information so obtained is worth while. Certainly, you will want a column for annual hours of usage so that your costs can be compared with those worked out by the agricultural experiment stations, equipment manufacturers, and agricultural engineers.

The equipment account is becoming the most significant one in the books as the manager is faced more and more with the question: Can I get a machine that will replace the labor I do not have, or that will do the job cheaper? In the very recent past, the big operator has tended to become critically overcapitalized in equipment. Inflation also lends its help. The machines do not seem to be as expensive as they are when the rubber dollar is considered. And, of course, owners who have substantial outside incomes quickly note that you cannot depreciate a hired hand but you can a combine.

Co-equal in importance is the labor account. At times it is more important when the owner looks at the costs on his neighbor's "dirt farm" and then at his own. No amount of business sagacity expended on a week-end or a once-a-month trip to the farm can make up for that sixteen-hour day of planning and dreaming ahead that the average owner-operator utilizes as he plows, milks, harvests, and sells.

An example showing the profitableness of studying the labor account may be found in the poultry account. Layers and broilers up to 500 birds are a nice side-line profit-maker on literally millions of owner-operated farms. Better than half our national poultry production comes from such farm flocks. But, as many an absentee owner has found to his sorrow, the same profit is not possible on his type of farm. The reason is, of course, that the owner-operator is charging nothing for his or his wife's time in caring for the birds. In his case, it is finding another bit of "chinking" (see Chapter 26) to fill in between the major logs of his time. The nonworking operator has to pay cash for time to care for the chicks. As he cannot usually make a profit that way, he has two choices: Get rid of poultry other than the flocks the hands keep for themselves on their own account, or build the enterprise into something that will justify one man's full-time attention. That will mean more expenditure for buildings, equipment, medicines, feed, and other items.

Probably more headaches and bad labor relations have come about on non-owner-operated farms as a result of the owner's attempt to put in side lines than from any other single cause. The owner cannot understand why his workmen do not want to be pestered with chickens, or milking a single cow, or making butter for the big house. The owner aggrievedly asks, "They get their own eggs or milk free, don't they?" Surely, but maybe they would rather buy them at the store and pay for somebody else to do the work.

Why shouldn't the hired man's wife make butter when she gets half and the cream comes to her free? (The owner just loves to take "butter from my own place, the kind you can't get in any store" to his friends in town.) He forgets labor cost. The hired man's wife is not interested in boasting about her butter. She is interested in the fact that she can make a great deal more money, hour for hour, in sewing, doing handcrafts, or just working for herself and her family. On one farm supervised by the authors, a little cost accounting showed that the wife who was making butter for half of it actually was working for eleven cents per hour when the current wage for any kind of help in that section was seventy-five cents per hour. In other words, as butter was selling locally for fifty cents a pound, she would have been better off running the tractor (which she did quite well) for forty-five minutes than spending the equivalent of almost five hours at butter-making to get her pound.

Too many absentee or nonworking farm owners think that their hired labor has a subsistence philosophy and only the owners have a cash or commercial philosophy. That erroneous idea has contributed not a little to the shortage of farm labor and the constant drift to the city of men who psychologically would be happier in farming. They want the right to work for cash, to buy their needs for cash, and to sell their spare time as they see fit—or even to waste it. It does not make any difference that they would be better off working the owner's way. Paternalism is a practice the farm laborer does not want any more than his counterpart on the assembly line wants it.

Hence, it is to the owner's own advantage to figure out costs before he proposes a new side line to the hands. It is to his own advantage to know just how much he actually has in those ears of sweet corn he takes to his friends, or that butter he provides for the luncheon of the Rotary Club. Often he could have saved money if he had imported the comestible from Czechoslovakia.

If cost accounting shows that you cannot compete with going market prices, as it will on only too many farms—providing the work is done honestly and not to "prove" that you are smarter than your brother club member—there are several avenues open. One: Get another manager. This is the usual first step. After a number of managers have failed to change red to black, then there is Two: Find a bigger "sucker" than yourself and sell out. Three, if you do not want to admit defeat or really do love the country, grass the place down and rent it to neighbors.

This last course may be unattractive if you are the stubborn kind. Then follow the lead of your many colleagues. Go in for "improving the breed" of any of the kinds and classifications of livestock that have an emotional appeal for you. The resulting net loss should be treated precisely as you treat your bill at the country club, for it is exactly the same sort of expenditure.

Maybe you still want to prove that you can make a go of farming without becoming a worker on your own place. Then specialty farming or processing is your best bet. Whatever you do, you will find that you need cost accounting more than your dirt-farmer neighbor if you are to make a profit. You are trying to combine soil, equipment, and somebody else's labor to make a profit in a business where you cannot lay men off when the market slumps. Your neighbor is trying to combine soil and equipment to make an opportunity to sell his own labor at what he hopes is a higher price on the long-term average than he could get working for someone else. Competitively he had you beat at the start, for his "wage" is variable with conditions, while the wages you pay are fairly well fixed despite conditions.

If by your own cost accounts you cannot make your farm pay and if your soil is good and your relation to market favorable, then you have the opportunity to lease the place to a working operator. If the lease is run under a farm-management service, your chances of being an owner with fewest possible headaches will be greatest. However, most of the management services will not undertake your offer if you want to run in any side lines. Some will not take your proposition if you live on the place. Possibly that circumstance suggests why so many nonfarmer owners fail.

A final word of caution to those who think they can beat the record-keeping game by having the bookkeepers from their own offices keep the farm accounts: Be sure that the bookkeeper knows the farm terminology: why a steer may be a cow but a cow is never a steer. Then be sure that the bookkeeper understands a few practical facts such as that gasoline in large storage compartments does evaporate. (Don't accuse your manager of theft before you are sure.) Almost all farm produce does shrink in storage. There is a certain amount of waste in transporting field produce and livestock to market. In short, if your city bookkeeper thinks his job is to prove that everyone on your farm is dishonest, he may succeed; but your labor turnover will set some sort of neighborhood record. This circumstance, incidentally, is usual where the nonfarm bookkeeper is part of the operation.

Accounts are not worth the paper they are written on if you do not understand them, what is behind them, and how they got that way.

Index

Corporation farms: 151
Cost accounting: 226, 237
Cost factors: proper combination, 201
Conrey, G. W.: 212 n.
Crop records: 223 ff.
Cunningham, J. B.: 143 n.
Curry, Norval H.: 96 n.

Damp, Patricia: x
Daniel, Harley: 40
Darrah, L. B.: 64
Davidson, J. Brownlee: 78 n., 87, 89 n.
Debt: relative to land quality, 157
Depreciation: how to avoid, 83, 86; methods of calculation, 84–85
Diminishing increment: 197
Diminishing returns: 195 ff.; applies to each cost factor, 197, 201; relation to costs and prices, 197
Diversification, vertical: 103
Diversified farming: 166, 188 ff.
Diversity: relative to equipment efficiency, 192; within specialization, 192
Doane, D. Howard: x, 77 n., 103, 190

Earnings: for debt payment, 149–50; on capital, 161–62
Economic environment: 185
Economics: more limiting than biology, 184
Electricity: cheapest hired hand, 99, 107; farms using, 99
Elliott, F. F.: 125 n.
Enterprise: selection, 192–94; balance, 208; response, 211
Erosion: slope and runoff, 35–36; geologic, 36; accelerated, 37; relative to vegetation, 37 ff.; strip cropping, 41 ff.
Equipment: mounted on rubber, 51; disadvantage to some farmers, 52, 75; labor-saving vs. cost-saving, 53; adapted to farm, 54 ff., 214–16; convenience of ownership, 58; combination machines, 59; manure spreader, 59; flame-weeder, 61; sprayers, 62;

relation to size of operation, 63–64; ownership vs. custom use, 67, 83–84; cotton picker, 69; removes labor peaks, 73–74, 165–66; tractors, 73 ff.; depreciation, 83 ff.; secondhand, 86–87; maintenance, 87; positive and negative considerations, 105–106; contribution to production, 107; displaces labor, 110; hay blower, 113; relation to diminishing returns, 200; records, 235

Family farm: 124–26; 139–41
Farm analysis: 204–19; purpose, 204; standards of comparison, 204–205; information needed, 219
Farm business equation: 176, 202
Farm: a term of indefinite meaning, 122; both home and job, 123; small, definition of, 123; Grandfather-farm, 124, 129; family size–family type, 124–25; family-commercial, definition of, 125; large-scale, definition of, 126; adequate, 126; adequate, as pacesetter, 127, 139; commercial, criterion of success, 127; objectives for successful operation, 131; refinanced every generation, 155
Farm inventory: 221
Farm Management, Office of: 174 n.
Farm management principles: 180–81
Farm operator (manager): only fixed item, 110; function of, 201–202
Farm organization: dictated by alternatives, 187
Farm size: not related to acres, 117–18; haphazard origin, 118; inadequate, 123–24, 129–37; adequate, 126, 138–50; part-time, 134–36; ways of enlarging, 134; why limited, 151–55; relation to capacity of manager, 143, 202
Farmer: his own boss, 109, 168; underemployed, 137; must finance his own job, 155

THE BUSINESS OF FARMING

HAS BEEN SET IN THE TEN POINT SIZE

OF LINOTYPE BASKERVILLE WITH

TWO POINTS BETWEEN LINES

AND HAS BEEN PRINTED UPON

WOVE ANTIQUE PAPER

UNIVERSITY OF OKLAHOMA PRESS

NORMAN